BE AN

# *Outrageous*

## OLDER MAN

## BE AN

# *Outrageous*

## OLDER MAN

*Action Guide for Men 50 and Beyond*

**Bard Lindeman**

Knowledge, Ideas & Trends, Inc.
KIT, the Positive Publisher
Manchester, Connecticut

Rights and permissions statement
© Bard Lindeman 1998
Cover art: Bob Josen Design
Text design and composition: Carrie Fradkin/C Design
Editor: Sonja Hakala
Copyeditor: Ruth Sylvester
Proofreader: K.K. Wilder
Front Cover Photo: Teryl Jackson

First published in 1998 by
Knowledge, Ideas & Trends, Inc.
KIT, The Positive Publisher
1131-0 Tolland Turnpike, Ste 175
Manchester, CT 06040
(800) 826-0529
www.booktrends.com
Knowledge, Ideas & Trends, Inc. books are available for bulk purchase and customization purchases by corporations and other organizations for promotion and premiums. Contact the special sales department at the above address.

Publisher's Cataloging-in-Publication
(Provided by Quality Books, Inc.)
Lindeman, Bard
    Be an outrageous older man : action guide for men 50 and beyond
    / Bard Lindeman. -- 1st. ed.
    p. cm.
    Includes bibliographical references.
    ISBN: 1-879198-24-X
    1. Men--United States-- Psychology. 2. Men--United States--Health and
    hygiene. 3. Aging. 4. Aged men-- Conduct of life. 5. Middle aged men--
    Conduct of life.  I. Title

    HQ1090.3.L56 1998    305.31
                         QB198-503


10 9 8 7 6 5 4 3 2 1

First edition
Published in the United States of America

*To my wife, Jan*

AUTHOR'S NOTE

It is fitting that a book written to men should take its inspiration from women. When she suggested there should be a companion to her *Be an Outrageous Older Woman,* author Ruth Harriet Jacobs was, in effect, assigning me the task of teaching senior men to shed old, musty ways, and, instead, to become outrageous in their maturity. Publisher Sandra Brown agreed this was a worthwhile cause and we were in business. Editor Sonja Hakala did her part, and to all three I owe my gratitude. I also owe a particular debt to those women who have added to my knowledge about aging. They are the late Maggie Kuhn, Jane Porcino, Elma Holder, Sarah Burger Greene, Carter Catlett Williams, Jane Brody, Betty Friedan, Caroline Bird, Katherine Jeter, Doris Aiken, and Kaylan Pickford. To my mind, these women, and others, have helped define the critical issues even as they have worked in the cause of a kinder, more just seniority for all Americans.

If any of the following sparks an opinion or two, please feel free to share your insights and stories with the author. You can reach him at:

**Bard Lindeman**
5428 Oxbow Road
Stone Mountain, GA 30087-1228
E-mail: Lindy@Abraxis.com

Publishing information about the books mentioned in *Be an Outrageous Older Man* is included in a bibliography at the end of the book.

# CONTENTS

*"There is nothing more beautiful in the world than a healthy wise old man."*

—Lin Yutang, Chinese philosopher

To be an older man in our society, which is given to the premise that youth is everything, is to know the meaning of considerable challenge. Yet being an older man gives you the opportunity to wear your years well, to feel the pride of being a tribal elder, a successful ager, someone who has lived and erred, but also someone who has contributed, and made our earth-station a better place. Being an older man in this day and age means having the opportunity to experience a range of positive emotions and feelings—the pride of being a loyal friend, a good husband, a good father, and, if you are blessed, a loving grandfather.

To be an older man in our society is to accept that you are a work in progress. Understand that you have years to go, and that not all your days will be good ones, but most will. Understand that you cannot slack off, or abdicate, or shrink from this challenge. Your family and friends need you because your experience and wisdom are in too short supply. Your community—your nation, too—needs you and your achievements, whether or not it is willing to make that connection.

It is the purpose of this opening essay to persuade you that, whatever your age—40, 50, 60, 70 or beyond—it is time you confront these new challenges, and understand and accept that growing older is neither an aberration nor an abomination. Instead, it is your gift, your opportunity for a second life, a time in which you have license to be different, non-conformist, yes, even outrageous.

Permit me to offer an example. In 1982 I set out to be the Ann Landers of the Graying Set. I wanted to write a widely-circulated, syndicated column. My subject: aging. I hoped that 400 newspapers would carry my column. I told my doubting friends, "Hey, I want to get paid for growing older."

Today I joke about "being paid so little for a job so difficult." The truth is the column idea was an outrageous idea, one that took me two years to sell to the *Chicago Tribune* group, Tribune Media Services. But that's beside the point because the column has brought professional satisfaction and untold joy, principally from new friends: responsive readers who write me from Poughkeepsie, NY, Hackensack and Atlantic City, NJ, Modesto, CA, Tucson, AZ, suburban Chicago, Melbourne, FL, and Pittsburgh, PA.

"In Your Prime," as the column is called, runs in some 45 papers and although the money would be pocket change to Ms. Landers, the giver of advice, I no longer care about profits. For I have a front-row seat on the world of aging. My true reward comes in knowledge and from the rich dialogue I carry on with my readership, including some very outrageous guys and gals. Nick and Gina Ellena of Oroville, CA, are two of these folks.

Thirty years ago, Gina Ellena served in the Peace Corps and was assigned to Nepal. When they were both in their 60s, the couple decided to return there. Nick, an amateur mountain climber, told me in a letter of how they survived monsoons, leeches, rain-swollen streams, and near-drowning: "It was a little bit of an adventure, a spectacular trip with great scenery. . . and we managed to see Mt. Everest. What an astonishingly huge and imposing creation it is."

After I read the letter from the Ellenas, I telephoned their house and learned that Nick, then 68 and a survivor of surgery for prostate cancer, was away at the gymnasium. "He's on the Stairmaster," Gina said. "He wants to climb to the base camp at the north side of Everest, and of course I support him in that wish."

"It's not all that high," Nick later told me. "It's only about 18,000 feet, and then you drop down to the camp. You get to see Everest and to hear those avalanches. That would be a real adventure."

Nick Ellena: one more male approaching a 70th birthday with big plans for the future. He dreams out loud about a trip halfway around the world to a small, isolated country where, $4,000 and a pocketful of leeches later, he can stand in awe at the base of one of the world's natural wonders.

To my way of thinking, this Californian, who was born in the Bronx, makes a valid point. Our seniority is the right time for us to climb a mountain, to correct wrongs, to plant a tree (or a forest), to sign an organ donor card that could assure a new start for someone in need. It's also the perfect time to launch an adventure, to travel to Central America to see butterflies, or Africa to photograph the elephants. It's the best time to repair a frayed relationship, to learn a new skill, to take up a musical instrument, to be someone very different, to reach out to a troubled youngster and become his (or her) mentor. You can even wear your cap backwards.

You cannot, you must not, kick back and play the role of some older man serving out his time in God's earthly waiting room. "Lots of people my age are sitting in Florida, and I could be one of them. I've earned it," the late Dr. George Sheehan wrote when he was in his 70s. "But I can go on because I feel I've never achieved what I could. If you take less than that view, you're finished." Sheehan was a cardiologist, then a writer, lecturer, distance runner, and philosopher, who wrote eloquently to millions of Americans for some thirty years on the matter of running and being.

George Sheehan, remarked one of his readers, "called us out to play." I, too, am urging that you come out and play. Play your game, whatever form or structure it takes. Play it hard, play it to the best of your ability and, please, play it outrageously. This injunction to turn a corner, to plow a new furrow, to push against the envelope is made, sincerely, with your interests at heart. With medical science to back me up, I assure you that you will age better and perhaps live longer, even as you win the admiration of friends and family, if you chart a new course and then set sail.

**GET**

*Outrageous*

# CHAPTER ONE

# Outrageous:

## RHYMES WITH COURAGEOUS

*"To know how to grow old is the master work
of wisdom, and one of the most difficult
chapters in the great art of living."*

—Henri Frederic Amiel

*utrageous* is nothing more than a code word for the independent, free-thinking, strong-willed mature adult. When you think about it, isn't it the outrageous men and women who get the job done while they keep our world interesting?

Isn't it outrageous for a brilliant, 61-year-old medical doctor to be blasted into space at the end of a jet-propelled rocket? Astronaut Story Musgrave didn't think so. Isn't it outrageous for onetime Surgeon General Dr. C. Everett Koop, now a private citizen and 80-plus years old, to declare war against obesity in the United States? And isn't it outrageous, and decidedly imprudent, for a 72-year-old George Bush, the former president, to parachute from an airplane 12,000 feet over the Arizona desert?

Isn't it outrageous for golfer Arnold Palmer, at 67, to battle back from prostate cancer, determined to play competitive golf again? And isn't it outrageous for a retired and unpublished schoolteacher to decide, in his 60s, to write the story of his impoverished childhood? Frank McCourt wrote *Angela's Ashes* anyway, and it became a Pulitzer prize–winning book, a bestseller, and received an award from the National Book Critics Circle.

By its very nature, journalism attracts outrageous individuals. Consider correspondent David Lamb. For nearly thirty years, he has reported from countries around the world. I rank Lamb as a prince among the tribe of newspaper iconoclasts, but as this *Los Angeles Times* newsman approached middle age, he underwent what you or I might interpret as a mid-life crisis. Here is how he characterized his torment: "I'd grown weary of putting out the trash Tuesday nights and worrying if my IRA was growing fast enough. I just wanted to do something outrageous."

What did this lion in a Lamb's body do? Did he rent a fistful of blue movies, or grow a beard, or vow never again to cut his suburban Virginia lawn? None of the above. Instead, he bicycled clear across the United States—alone, from the backyard of his Arlington home to the California coast.

On an Indian reservation in Oklahoma, Lamb was asked by a young Pawnee man dressed in the telltale baggy pants and backward cap of city kids why he didn't drive cross country instead of bicycle. Lamb's answer is perfect for those of us who espouse the cause of being outrageous. "I tried to explain the compensation of unexpected encounters along untraveled roads. I mentioned the rush of wind in my face, of being unhurried, of growing stronger, and being close to the land and feeling the rhythm of the road in my bones. It's just a kick."

Indeed, being older and outrageous is a kick. I first heard that idea articulated during an interview with the late Maggie Kuhn, who was an early spiritual force behind the pro-aging movement in this country. This diminutive, white-haired woman, with her bifocals and sharp wit, helped found the Gray Panthers. "Aging is not a disease," she once said. "It is strength and survivorship. We are not wrinkled babies. We're a new breed of older women and men."

In my mind's eye I still see this heroine, in eminently sensible shoes, standing at a lectern lambasting those who would practice injustice, inflexibility, and ineptitude. She shored up her measured words with this philosophy.

1. One person can make a difference.

2. Age does not give anyone the license to retire from life, or withdraw from the fray.

3. The frailty that comes to the body over time need not impair the spirit.

"We are the tribal elders," she taught. "We're concerned about the tribe's survival. Our job is to secure the future for the young."

When I met Kuhn, I was editor of *50 Plus* magazine in New York and was questioning everything about the process of aging and what it meant. Maggie Kuhn was physically weakened because of arthritis and cancer, but she continued to preach her positive message. "We've become free to burst out and be truly creative," she told me. "It's wonderful to make use of the knowledge and experience that come after living a long, full life. When I turned 76, I made a resolution to do something outrageous—I mean, at least once a week."

Another disciple of Maggie Kuhn, and an authentic outrageous older woman, is Ruth Harriet Jacobs, Ph.D., of proper, historic Wellesley, MA. Dr. Jacobs, who has credentials as a sociologist, poet, gerontologist, activist, lecturer, author, and college professor, chronicles her outrageousness in the book *Be An Outrageous Older Woman*. This popular work plainly struck a chord with women readers. "At age 66, I learned that if you are outrageous enough, good things happen," Jacobs wrote. "You stop being invisible, and become validated."

Ruth Jacobs is a serious social scientist, not just some crank with a chip on her shoulder. When I wrote a column or two on her book, we became friends, soul mates. One day, after a rollicking and successful road trip speaking before several groups of active seniors, Dr. Jacobs picked up her phone. "You should write a companion book on the outrageous older male," she advised. "Definitely, one is needed."

Desiring always to be cooperative and pleasing to women of a certain age, I immediately agreed to continue to be outrageous—this time in print. My three adult children said in chorus, "Perfect. Now you get to write about your life history, because you've always been outrageous."

Let's agree that being outrageous is not being irresponsible. In a number of ways, being outrageous is synonymous with being courageous. Here, in capsule form, is how you go about being outrageous:

1. You volunteer, seeking to help others.

2. You take charge of your health, acknowledging that you are a responsible person.

3. You stay involved with younger people, refusing to become isolated and alienated.

4. You are a good friend to your friends, both men and women.

5. You stand up for yourself, making the statement that "I'm older, but I'm good. I count for something, and don't you dare direct your ageism my way."

6. You laugh at yourself often, because you're good-humored and funny.

7. You continue to work, either at your old job, a second career, or your volunteer activities.

8. You stay current with the world, reading a newspaper, books, magazines. You're a good conversationalist.

9. You exercise and also have a hobby that keeps you active.

10. You're good to and proud of your life-partner.

11. You concede that you're getting older, but you're a fighter and you've vowed not to give in. You're going to make every single outrageous day count!

# A Manifesto
# for the Outrageous Older Man

The reader's letter to my syndicated column came at me, juicy and fat, like a fast ball over the heart of the plate. "You seem to hold to the idea that some older men (and women) quit on life," this correspondent began. "You imply they give in to the dullness and frailty of age. What would you have them do?"

Here is how I answered this inquirer. "In a word, fight. None of us is guaranteed a tulip garden with room service. And yes, aging is synonymous with struggle. I promise you that the enlightened highway leading to seniority is marked by signposts encouraging you to struggle. . . and struggle hard."

There's nothing especially outrageous about this premise. It's just old world common sense, the kind of advice your taciturn but sage old grandfather might offer.

Robin Marantz Henig, medical author and friend, has written, "Either consciously or subconsciously, some older people will bend to the subtle social pressures to be crotchety, withdrawn, asexual, passive, dependent, depressed—not only because they believe they're supposed to, but because it's easier than fighting."

Well, this book is all about fighting and growing, principally because this behavior is time-tested, and is offered with your best interest in mind. It was the renowned social scientist Erik Erikson who preached the merits and efficacy of "vital involvement" for all our years. Further, the poet Philip James Bailey wrote, "We live in deeds, not years; in thought, not breaths; he most lives who thinks most—feels the noblest—acts the best."

More than two thousand years ago, Cicero, the Roman statesman and orator, said, "It's not age that is at fault, but rather our attitude toward it." It is time to repair our attitudes—and to construct new lives as outrageous, and courageous, older guys. ◆

# CHAPTER TWO

# Relax!

## AGING IS NOT A FOUR-LETTER WORD

*"If there were no older men,
there would be no civilized states at all."*

—Cicero

There is both positive and negative aging. Negative aging, I'm convinced, begins in the mind. The majority of Americans learn negative aging behavior from our culture. We are told that we're expected to work long and hard and then, sorry, you rock in your chair a while—just before you die.

We're reminded constantly that the body just wears out and the gloom-spreaders report if you're really lucky, the mind goes after the body fails. Think about all the powerful verbal cues that surround us describing the horrors of that first wrinkle, graying hair, baldness, retirement, a pesky prostate, sagging body parts, dentures, and the dowager's hump.

All of this amounts to negative reinforcement. To be old, says this thinking, is to suffer. I don't buy it, and neither should you.

Yes, I accept that change and hardships come with aging—but that is only one part of a far larger story. I believe that if you're willing to make the effort, the aging chapter of your life remains yours to craft. Popular author Deepak Chopra, M.D., who dresses better than I do and has a few more readers, writes in *Ageless Body, Timeless Mind,* "Every day we are either learning or unlearning what it means to age. Will we try new ways of living, or will we leave our bodies and minds to the crushing weight of cultural condition which, over time, leaves us broken, ill and, yes, old?"

Then there are the words of that less sophisticated prophet, Elroy "Satchell" Paige. This incomparable baseball pitcher, who was forced to spend most of his long career in the Negro Leagues because of blatant racial segregation, once asked, "How old would you be if you didn't know how old you was?" This marvelous, all-American quotation remains the perfect squelch to those hung up on age-specific chronology.

As senior adults, and outrageous older men, we are well-advised not to take life too seriously. Further, we have license to keep alive within us that inner child. "We are intended to remain in many ways childlike," anthropologist Ashley Montagu once wrote. "We were never intended to grow up into the kind of adults most of us have become. We are designed. . . to grow and develop in ways that emphasize rather than minimize childlike traits."

An educator as well as a shrewd observer, Montagu suggests we have only to watch children to understand the essential nature of fun and abandon. To children, curiosity is as natural as breathing. From curiosity comes playfulness, open-mindedness, the willingness to experiment, flexibility, humor, energy, and, of course, imagination. To my mind, none of these qualities is precluded by aging. Therefore, we outrageous guys have every right to test ourselves by asking the following question: "How many of these behaviors do I see within myself today?"

Because confession is good for the soul, I admit that I sneak into swimming pools. Just like some kid, I find a way to cross the line from outside to inside because I like to swim and I especially enjoy trying out different pools. Much like the boy who collects baseball cards, or the matron proud of her row of antique clocks, I collect pools where I have beaten the gate, so to speak.

Where have I violated house rules? For years while living in Florida, I "borrowed" a Holiday Inn pool ("For guests only," read the sign I ignored) and just off the ocean at Lake Worth, I favored a saltwater pool that was the property of a Ramada Inn, or some such. I was almost always the only one swimming.

A major conquest was a pool on the Stanford University campus. "Suppose I were to sneak in there?" I asked a professor, someone half my age. He answered, "They would consider that extremely bad form." Five minutes later I was in the college pool, alone and thrilled at my hijinks. I wondered what Ashley Montagu would say to me now?

You see, being an outrageous older man has both responsibilities ("What zany things have you done lately?") and privileges. What better time for sport and nonsense than in these senior years? I mean, who was I bothering? And everywhere I turned, someone was telling me to exercise.

Now another of my life-teachers has been Dr. Edward Rosenbaum, internist and author. Ed is a recovered cancer patient who takes infinite pleasure from each new day and his circle of longtime friends.

"A fountain of youth flows within ourselves," he once told me when he was in his seventies. "Its an ever-renewing current of life, a constant miracle that most of us are too busy or otherwise distracted to truly appreciate. Perhaps only with age and the knowledge that time has grown more precious are some of us able to recognize the fountain, and to cherish all over again our capacity to think, feel, laugh, and love."

A natural storyteller, this man of medicine has spent a professional life listening to his patients. Here is a story out of the Rosenbaum file that belongs in any essay on positive aging.

Nearing 70, a gardener goes shopping for flowering trees and pauses next to a stand of magnolias. The young nursery owner walks over and says, "Sir, those trees aren't for you. It takes that tree at least ten years before it really blooms." The senior gardener quickly replies, "Good, I'll take three."

Dr. Rosenbaum continues his narrative, adding, "My friend lived to see his magnolia trees bloom spectacularly. For a number of springs before he died, my friend enjoyed his special magnolia trees."

Ed Rosenbaum's friend, and indeed most outrageous men I know, are stubborn as they zealously guard their convictions. Moreover, they will never allow someone to tell them they're too old. Writing in *Say Yes To Aging*, Dr. Alex Comfort refers to this "bloody-mindedness." He then explains this is a British Army term and contains overtones of "heroic obstinacy in not being put down." He calls it the "chief adaptive character of man" and the "ultimate resource of the older person."

Comfort also quotes the Welsh poet Dylan Thomas who, of course, wrote, "Do not go gentle into that good night."

With this bloody-minded spirit at the fore, let me offer you the Outrageous Older Man's ten commandments—injunctions to help you remain heroic, yet well liked. For the record, I first received the commandments in a slightly different form from Dorothy Barlow, a widow who soon will turn 100. She is the oldest reader of my column and periodically writes me from Florence, AZ, where she lives on a desert cactus farm.

1. Thou shalt narrate stories of past adventures two times only, unless pressured by popular request.

2. Thou shalt not interrupt thy spouse's stories.

3. Thou shalt be socially agreeable at all times because visitors are to an older gentleman what a hot meal is to a homeless person.

4. Thou shalt daily be engaged in some labor, so the evening hours be seasoned with the sweet satisfaction of accomplishments.

5. Thou shalt nourish thy sense of humor, lest it wither and die.

6. Thou shalt smile, lest the muscles of thy face freeze into a permanent frown.

7. When the opportunity for laughter comes, laugh with others and not at them.

8. On hearing that a grandchild (or even a close friend) has entered into a live-in relationship without benefit of clergy, thou shalt refrain from making clucking sounds or rolling of the eyes. Verily, it is none of thy business.

9. Thou shalt not listen to any nonsense about being old, dull, slow-witted, weak, bent, infirm, or crotchety, for verily it is ageism—the work of warped minds.

10. Thou shalt remember that thou art an Outrageous Older Man, who is a doer of deeds, an achiever, a worker in the name of good. Thou mayest rage and deliver verbal broadsides but never—no never—carp, complain, or whine. Amen.

# CHAPTER THREE

# On Becoming

## OUTRAGEOUS

*"It is always in season
for old men to learn."*

—Aeschylus

From my high school days forward, I knew that I must be a writer. I never wanted to do anything else. For me, that meant starting as a reporter for newspapers and, when I was ready, becoming a magazine writer. I didn't allow myself the dream of becoming an author.

My freshman English teacher at Westwood High School in New Jersey told me I had a flair for words. I was hooked. It was that simple.

I've been a soldier-reporter for the *Pacific Stars & Stripes* during the Korean War, a newsman in Texas for the Associated Press, a street reporter in New York for the old *The World-Telegram & The Sun,* a medical writer for the *Miami Herald,* a contributing writer for the *Saturday Evening Post,* and a health editor at *Family Circle* magazine. I've also edited two monthly magazines. In Chicago, I directed *Today's Health* for the American Medical Association and in the 1980s I was editor of *50 Plus* magazine. It's now called *New Choices: Living Even Better After 50.*

I like to joke that I am "a gypsy of journalism." I enjoyed working in the city room of a newspaper, but when I moved into the magazine world, I found it fascinating and more rewarding. I had the good fortune to begin my career during newspaper's better days when there were seven competing papers in New York City. I also had the good fortune to jump to the *Saturday Evening Post* at an especially exciting time.

The *Post* was caught in a circulation and advertising war with its principal rivals, *Life* and *Look*. That print war, however, was nothing compared to the competition from television. Long-winded stories about the death of reading were common in those days and the word along the corridors of the magazine was "Write fast." According to the financial pages, the *Post's* parent company, Curtis Publishing Company, lost some $40 million in just four years. Signs of early death were abundant, but we contributing writers ran full tilt, pretending to be immune.

I traveled somewhere new every month, reporting on the civil rights march through Selma, AL, the Alaskan earthquake that devastated Anchorage, the heinous late night murder of Kitty Genovese in New York, when more than sixty neighbors listened to her piercing screams, but did nothing to help. I chronicled an oil boom in, of all places, Ohio. I spent weeks proving an alleged amnesiac a fraud, and months on the story of a pious yet vengeful Kentucky man who tracked down his father's hit-and-run killer. It took Welby Lee twenty-eight years to get his man—and see to it this malefactor would spend a year and a day in jail.

During these frenetic years, I also wrote two nonfiction books: *Strangers On A Bridge,* with spy-swap lawyer James B. Donovan (he traded U.S. pilot Gary Powers for KGB colonel Rudolf I. Abel on the bridge that once connected East and West Berlin) and *The Twins Who Found Each Other*. Even more importantly, I became the father of three wonderful, imaginative children whom I love with all my heart.

In 1970, with my wife's encouragement, I took a well-paying editorial job with the American Medical Association and moved my family to suburban Chicago. I assumed the title of editor-in-chief of *Today's Health,* a lackluster magazine, and then set about a long rebuilding process. Nineteen months into this experiment, my life turned upside down and sideways.

My wife complained of what the doctors termed "stomach distress." The problem, undiagnosed after weeks of tests, was especially bad following meals. Adele Kathleen Mullen Lindeman was just 40 when she entered West Suburban Hospital in Oak Park, IL, for "exploratory surgery." Eight days later, Del Lindeman, who had been uncommonly healthy and always stoical about minor ailments, was dead of peritonitis, a virulent infection.

I had been told to wait outside her room because she was suffering with stomach gas. I waited and I paced. Twenty minutes later, a nurse walked toward me and I knew. I knew I had been lied to. I knew I had been a fool to believe them. I knew my wife, the mother of our children, was dead. I knew that my Del, whom I had met when we were giddy kids at Vermont's Middlebury College, an idyllic place to fall in love, was gone from me. I whirled around instinctively and punched the wall with my right hand. I broke a knuckle, yet felt nothing in that hand for days.

As a confused, lonely, numb widower, with children ages 8, 12, and 15, my life course was plain. I had to take care of the kids. I found solace and escape in the magazine which, under the day-to-day direction of editor David Sendler, was attracting talented contributors and showing signs of remarkable progress.

Together, David and I stretched the limits of a publication which had been long regarded as an insipid magazine for doctors' waiting rooms. It was inevitable that we would eventually run afoul of the American Medical Association's leadership. One example of our "stretching" should suffice. We did a story about a one-day procedure for hernia repair, a procedure for which most patients spent five days in the hospital. After the story was published, I was taking phone calls and answering intemperate letters from doctors who were protesting, "I won't have that rag in my waiting room. My patients are demanding to know why they have to spend five days in the hospital when you idiots write that it's a one-day procedure. Don't you understand, Mr. Lindeman, my dues pay your salary. You work for me!"

There were, at that time, some 166,000 physician members of the AMA and each one had a button that, when pressed, lit up in my office. I was often summoned to the corner office during my five years at *Today's Health* to receive a sharp lecture about my sins of commission and/or omission. My customary response was, "Well, that's not the way we did it at the *Saturday Evening Post*." This excuse worked a couple of times. But no one wins a contest of wills against the intransigent AMA.

On a gray January Friday in 1975, I made my last trip to the communications director's office. I had written four newspaper pieces on a freelance basis on the crisis of health care costs. The AMA did not approve.

"Withdraw those articles," I was told, "or put on your hat and coat." My eldest child Les, then 18, said, "Did you tell them, Dad, you never wear a hat?"

Later that afternoon, I was handed a note directing me to be out of the building by 5:00 P.M.

For several weeks, my firing was a *cause célèbre*. The details made the United Press news wire, Studs Terkel had me as a guest on his radio show, and the *Washington Post* ran a story headlined "Taking the Crisis Out of Today's Health." The AMA alternately insisted that I had lied or that I wasn't permitted to write as a freelancer. My response was uniform. "The AMA doesn't enjoy criticism from without, and they surely aren't going to abide criticism from within."

In the space of five short years, I had lost the wife who kept me grounded and the family intact, and I had lost my job suddenly. My first inclination was to panic, but, with my three children as my rudder, I held firm to a daily regimen and returned to freelance writing. Then the telephone rang. The *Miami Herald* was looking for a medical writer. Was I interested? In a heartbeat, I accepted the offer, moving the family to south Florida where I jumped back into the mad whirl of daily journalism.

The *Herald*, the flagship paper of the successful Knight-Ridder chain, was now about to get a graying journalistic gypsy who was, among other things, a battle-scarred boat-rocker. One outrageous dude.

# CHAPTER FOUR

# So Many Causes,

## SO LITTLE TIME

*"Growing old is no more than a bad habit
which a busy man has no time to learn."*

—André Maurois

When I lived in south Florida, I kept hearing this tired line: "Miami Beach is God's waiting room." It was meant to be humorous, of course, and reflected the unarguable fact that the thin strip of condominiums and sand, which is a real estate appendage of the city of Miami, attracted an inordinate number of very old women and men in the 1970s. Shuffleboard, rocking chairs, and nightly bingo were staples of life on The Beach.

As the *Miami Herald*'s new boy in town, I determined to find and interview someone on Miami Beach who was truly *waiting to die*. A social service agency produced my man, and I shall always remember Edward Scanlon and his one-room world, complete with hot plate and stained wallpaper. It was just like a scene from a T.S. Eliot poem.

The lead to my story read, "Edward Scanlon sits alone in a south Miami Beach hotel room smaller than some prison cells. He is 84. He is waiting to die."

During the interview, I listened as this stooped, melancholy, retired Chicago fireman explained why he waited, impatiently, to die. Once, he had lived to fish from the Miami causeways, but now, ailing from a combination of infirmities—degenerative bone disease in both hips, failing eyesight, and perhaps athrosclerosis (hardening of the arteries)—Scanlon seldom left his room. Whatever family he had no longer cared to be involved in his constricted and obviously unhappy life. A buddy who lived down the hall had to help him to the bathroom during the night.

"I been parked in this room going on four years," he told me. "It's just a matter of sitting and waiting for the end, waiting for them to come and get me."

When I asked about his fishing, he brightened. "I almost never missed a day off the MacArthur Causeway," he said. "Met a lot of good friends there."

As I looked about his cramped, soiled cloister, I counted four items of particular importance to this aged pensioner: two radios (I couldn't bring myself to ask why two), a hot plate ("I don't bother much for food") and a handwritten letter instructing that Edward Scanlon be cremated and his ashes "be dumped from that bridge where fishing was my whole life."

The *Miami Herald* is a big city newspaper, notable for young talent striving to make it so they can move on to New York, Washington, Los Angeles, or Television Land. The ruling cliché in our city room was "You're only as good as your *next* story." Meaning that you had to keep hustling, ever on the prowl for tomorrow's piece. So I put Ed Scanlon on page one for a few editions and then lost track of him, along with his wish to die quickly and, as he put it, "without fuss."

What I didn't lose sight of was the depth and breadth of the

Story of Aging, USA. It is, without doubt, the best and biggest story of my long career in reporting. In this country, the story about aging is driven in large part by the all-American desire to live long and to live each day to the maximum. While people have always had the desire to live long, our ability to reach that goal is new because of advances in medicine, nutrition, and technology.

Alan Pifer, the Carnegie Foundation's president emeritus, is an observer of the changing landscape of aging. He writes, "Few Americans realize their country is in the midst of a demographic revolution that, sooner or later, will affect every individual and every institution in the society. That revolution," Pifer continues, "is the inexorable aging of our population."

He predicts that before the revolution has run its course "the impact will have been at least as powerful as that of any of the great economic and social movements of the past. . . such as the conquest and closing of the frontier, the successive waves of European immigration. . . or, from more recent times, the civil rights and women's movements, the revolution in sexual mores, and the decay of many of our large urban centers."

Pifer has been trying to alert our policy makers and politicians, explaining to them that the future is not preordained. "Population aging holds within it the promise of a much better society for all of us or, paradoxically, a far worse one," Pifer wrote. And the choice is ours to make.

After three years in the American tropics, I made my choice, returning to my natal city of New York to write exclusively about aging. It's a fascinating, ever-changing, and dynamic story which reaches out and touches on matters of money, health and medicine, housing, jobs, second careers, sexuality and romance, long-term marriages, lifelong learning, travel, hobbies, adventure, retirement, politics and government, and life's penultimate bonus, grandchildren.

In 1984, I began writing my weekly column, "In Your Prime." At first it was syndicated by Associated Press Newsfeatures. "If we can get fifty papers to subscribe," I was told, "the column will make money." Before that first year was history, 114 newspapers, most of them in small cities, were publishing 650 of my words on aging each week. At almost the same time, I became the editor of *50 Plus* magazine, a struggling, insecure monthly publication going out to 280,000 consumers, most of whom wished, as one woman suggested, that we would send it in a plain wrapper.

Early on, I reached the determination that if you were going to be *in* aging, you should also be *for* aging. There are those who are aggressive about making money from older consumers, while the scientists only want to study them. As a journalist, however, I chose to become a watchdog, a cop on the beat. I told my *50 Plus* staff that it was our responsibility to represent and speak out on behalf of those who struggle each day to get by on fixed incomes, those who have been downsized or forced to take early retirement because of age bias, and those who are battling through grief as widows or widowers.

In addition, there are the Edward Scanlons who are beaten down by life's vicissitudes and exist in one-room efficiencies with the bathroom down the hall. Is this tolerable? Is this the best we can do in the United States? I think not. Then there are the 1.8 million women and men who must finish out their lives in nursing homes. These forgotten folk are truly the legion of the isolated and the alienated. Too often they are drugged or bound in restraints simply because they are confused or agitated or, in the muddled minds of their keepers, require more care than is available at that particular moment.

As I covered the Story of Aging USA, I quickly adopted all these causes, and more. My involvement as a journalist is but one part of the larger story, however. Throughout this book, it is my intent to enlist your empathy and your support. We who stand up for our brothers and sisters in the Great Gray Legion need all the help we can get.

Keep an open mind, please, as well as an open heart, as you make your way through these pages. Permit me to urge you to become outrageous by finding a cause to champion.

Remember, there are so many causes. . . and so little time.

# CHAPTER FIVE

# Fighting Ageism:

## IT'S WORK FOR A LIFETIME!

*"The chronic illness faced by a majority of older Americans is not arthritis or high blood pressure, but the much more insidious disease known as ageism."*

—Aljean Harmetz, author and journalist, in *New Choices* magazine

Ageism is prejudice, plain and simple. Like racism, which it resembles, ageism is based on fear and ignorance. It is the foul work of unthinking people who persist in spreading their hurtful foolishness.

Dr. Robert N. Butler, in his Pulitzer prize–winning exposé, *Why Survive? Being Old in America,* defined ageism as "a systematic stereotyping of and discrimination against people because they are old, just as racism and sexism accomplish this with skin color and gender."

It was Butler, a world leader in the promotion of research into normal aging, who first coined the word "ageism," a term which has appeared in most dictionaries since 1970. Now if you are 60 years or older and have not felt the sting of age bias, you are the rare person, perhaps the exception. Look around you. Examples of ageism are everywhere.

Ageism is spread throughout the health care industry. To make the point, Bob Butler tells the story of the tough, older man who complains his left leg gives him pain. His doctor says it's because he's lived too long. "At your age," the doctor says, "what do you expect?"

"Well, how come my right leg doesn't hurt me" asked the stubborn senior patient. "Both them legs is the same age."

During the time I was editor of *Today's Health* magazine, I suggested to the publisher, the American Medical Association, that it would be a good idea to open a free clinic in the headquarters building. Even hang a banner over the entrance saying "America's Doctors Make House Calls." After vetoing the idea as impractical, one of the AMA executives said, "Do you know how long it takes those people to take off their clothes, and then put them back on?" By *those people,* he meant older adults.

At *50 Plus* magazine, we did a story describing how oftentimes doctors spend far less time with older patients, and there also is less conversation between these patients and their physicians. The bottom line—in too many instances, ageism leads to poor medical practice.

Ageism is a favorite pastime on television. Consider how infrequently an older person is cast in a positive role. Horace B. Deets, executive director of the American Association of Retired Persons, once said, "Television makes invisible one-third of the adult population—68 million senior men and women."

When the typical American child is born into a home where TV is on for seven hours and forty-one minutes a day (the national average), he or she sees approximately 353 characters a week. How can we expect that person to grow to maturity thinking positively about older adults?

A writer for *50 Plus* magazine uncovered the fact that a typical public library system has 660 children's books and 84 percent of them contain *no* older characters in them. Following the publication of that article, I wrote a newspaper column launching a campaign to change this. "Today's children don't know much about us graying Americans," I wrote, "and this is wrong, even shameful."

The column quoted an expert on the subject, Edward F. Ansello, Ph.D., of the University of Maryland: "Having no older people says something to the children. . . that old is uninteresting. It's a stereotype by absence."

I went on to urge readers to buy or borrow books that "teach about aging in a positive sense, books that have something to say about the joys, the challenges, the frustrations of growing older in a country that worships youth. Meaning, that you and I can tell our kids the truth." The magazine followed up with a list of recommended books and we encouraged readers to complain to their libraries about this negligence.

My enduring memory of that experience is Dr. Ansello's analysis of what university researchers found when they interviewed children ages 3 to 11. He explained how the kids felt warmth, even love, for older folks. Yet the kids were absolutely convinced "all older people didn't do much and they didn't know much."

That's ageism, plain and simple.

The world of fashion is built upon the transcendent premise that youth is the answer to all dilemmas. Write me, please, the next time you see more than one older woman model in a department store catalog. Better still, go shopping for a stylish bathing suit for your wife. Good luck.

In a nation in love with youth and vigor, the sad ballad of ageism is an increasingly familiar tune. It also continues to be an underreported news story. Therefore, I was encouraged to read veteran journalist Aljean Harmetz's powerful 1997 article for *New Choices* magazine. She wrote, "When only the young are valued, older people can fail to get the health care that would save their lives, or make their lives less painful. When only young workers are promoted, and older workers are discarded, the impact on a generation that wants to contribute to society is immeasurable."

Aljean is a former reporter for *The New York Times* in Los Angeles and she told stories about teachers, actors, screenwriters, and others who had been bruised by ageism. She wrote, "Up to now, ageism has not been a hot topic, except to people affected by it, and the very fact of society's indifference diminishes the older citizen." The editor of *New Choices,* David Sendler, entitled Aljean's piece "A Disease America Won't Cure—and Should."

I've been banging away at this maddening injustice since 1982 and have railed against intolerance of the elderly in my column and in magazine articles. When I challenged the readers of my column to report incidents of bias, a woman wrote to me about her husband. She described him as "a hard-working draftsman who at age 65 suddenly found himself jobless. That was a year ago," she said. "Now my life-partner is sure of only one thing, that he is the unfair victim of age discrimination. I won't ever admit this to him, but I no longer disagree when he states, 'I may never find another job.' He also says things like, 'What's the matter with these people? Can't they see I'm not old?'"

When *50 Plus* magazine ran a two-part series on ageism, I decided to do my editor's essay on bias in the workplace. I traveled to AARP headquarters in Washington, D.C., and met with lawyer Christopher G. Mackaronis, then head of the association's worker equity department. He handed me a Gallup poll which showed 95 percent of those who believed they had been discriminated against had done nothing—taken no action at all.

"When we asked them why," Mackaronis told me, "The largest percentage said they took no action because they didn't think it would do any good." Confused and at loose ends, thousands persist in sending long letters to AARP filled with melancholy details. After I read through a half-dozen of these sad examples, I wrote, "Every business day the plaintive narratives reach the Washington, D.C., headquarters of AARP. 'They write here,' a researcher explained, 'because they just don't know where to turn.'"

"With few exceptions," I continued, "these correspondents have been touched, indeed scarred, by age bias. Significantly, many don't even realize they have been victimized, that they have been prematurely, arbitrarily, unlawfully forced from the workplace. . . "

The lifelong battle against ageism has to begin with ourselves. Each of us has to make a stand. Each of us should pretend that we have a syndicated column to write today and quickly gather material for this editorial battle. Each of us has to say, "I'm okay. I'm older, yes. But I'm good and I count." Some believe that older people complain too much. I disagree. I believe, fervently, that we don't complain enough.

Dr. Alex Comfort, critic and author, wrote in his book *Say Yes to Aging,* "Like racism, ageism needs to be met by information, contradiction, and, when necessary, confrontation. People who are being victimized have to stand up for themselves in order to put it down."

With the exception of a mere handful of successful age bias suits, we've allowed American industry and society in general to denigrate our contributions. We've allowed, even welcomed, the dynamic known as "early retirement." Well, here come the baby boomers and millions of them will want to stay in the work force. They'll have to, for economic reasons. We're about to see these feisty, inventive boomer men and women take on the enemy known as age bias. It will be a collision worth witnessing. Meantime, we senior men will undoubtedly profit from this struggle. It cannot happen soon enough for this outraged observer.

# The
# *Outrageous*
# *Mind*

# CHAPTER SIX

# The Incredible

## AGING BRAIN

*"When younger people forget, they are busy.*
*When older people forget, they are old. There is*
*a term for this kind of thinking. It's ageism."*

—Randy Georgemiller, Ph.D.,
neuropsychologist

My son, the doctor, had met me at Miami International Airport, and now suddenly we were lost in the concrete caves known as parking garages. Or rather, the Paul Lindeman, M.D., family van was temporarily among the missing.

"I thought it was here, right here!" said this busy emergency room physician who works 12-hour shifts, and then returns, exhausted and drained, to his mortgaged home, wife Suzy, and their energetic redheads, Melissa and Stephanie.

"What are you laughing at?" he said, with an edge to his voice. "It's not funny."

What is undeniably humorous, and a little sad, is that if I had forgotten where I parked the car, early senility might have been a suspect. Yet if a stressed boomer, still in his 30s, forgets where he parks his car, society chalks it up to normal forgetfulness.

The melancholy truth is that each of us—adults ranging from age 40 to 100—lives today in the long, forebidding shadow cast by the brain anomaly Dr. Bob Butler labeled "our twentieth-century scourge." He refers, of course, to Alzheimer's, also known as the mind-robbing disease. Named for the German physician who first diagnosed it, this baffling disruption of the central nervous system has no detectable cause and, far worse, no known cure or even an effective therapy to relieve the symptoms.

The harsh facts about the disease are well known. Alzheimer's has become our fourth leading killer disease. At any one time, an estimated four million Americans (the majority of them women) are victims of this frightening disease. (Trust me, *victim* is the correct choice of noun here.) The average length of time one travels the downward path of this degenerative process can be eight, ten, even fifteen years. No one recovers from Alzheimer's.

In 1988, Robin Marantz Henig, a well-respected medical writer and author, published *The Myth of Senility*, in which she wrote, "Most people do not go senile, no matter how long they live." The book sold so well, it was later reissued.

I choose to emphasize this news and say, more than once, that the aging brain is a good brain, a master organ capable of coping and of remarkable creativity for the length of its life.

Let's begin our good news report with words from the specialists. Dr. Zavan S. Khachaturian, a brain scholar, is fond of explaining how "most notions about aging and the brain are based on folklore rather than fact." Douglas Powell, a psychologist at Harvard University, adds, "The only thing you can assume about a 65- or 75-year-old is how many candles will be on their birthday cake." Dr. Gene Cohen, M.D. and Ph.D., a psychiatrist who urges large-scale creativity throughout life and was once the acting director of the National Institute on Aging, points to the fact that scientists are disproving the myths or false beliefs about what happens when the mind ages. He states, "Increasingly, those changes that were said to be 'aging' are now thought to be due to illness."

Having put the record straight, it's time to concede that, yes, the human brain does change through the years. It shrinks, losing about 10 percent of its weight, and some large cells (neurons) wither. However, the full importance of these changes is difficult to interpret because so little is known, even today, of how the brain actually works.

Here, though, is what can be reported. The brain operates as both an electrical and biochemical instrument. The normal brain at maturity has 100 billion neurons, many with thousands of connections (synapses) through which they send signals up and down our bodies. These signals (impulses, thoughts, reactions, etc.) travel from synapse to synapse electrically, producing chemical changes which, in effect, become memory.

As we age, most people experience some slowing down in the ability to remember. This is due in part to a loss of neurons. It's believed the brain loses 100,000 neurons a day. The cells simply die, and unlike others in the body, will not be replaced because they cannot divide or reproduce. So by the time you reach 65, you may have lost 20 percent of your 100 billion cells which accounts for the brain's shrinkage. You still possess 80 billion neurons, however, and you may have grown more synapses. In other words, your brain is being kind to you. It's compensating for the loss of neurons, finding new and clever ways to function, to communicate, and even to store memory.

Much of what I have learned on this fascinating subject was taught me by Dr. Cohen. This engaging and learned researcher believes that "aging precludes neither productivity nor the display of creative accomplishment. Creativity in later life," he has written, "is underrecognized, underreported, and underutilized."

In his book, *The Brain in Human Aging*, Dr. Cohen encourages us all to push ourselves, to challenge our intellect. He quotes playwright Sean O'Casey, who wrote at the age of 77, "Does creativity decline with age? No. Activity is bound to be less, but the creativity of an active mind goes on. . . I have just finished a play; I am working on a new book; and here, now, I am telling those who may be a little younger, or as old as myself, to go on too."

That surely is good counsel—to go on. So do your creative thing and do it outrageously well while you cavort, smile, laugh, and find the bliss in your quest.

# An Idle Mind:
## The Devil's Plaything

With each new bundle of mail addressed to my column, I find the same question—"Is there nothing we can do to head off memory loss? Seems that just about everyone I know is complaining of this problem."

Well, the brain's food is *education,* writes my friend Ron Kotulak. In his astounding and under-appreciated book *Inside The Brain,* this eminent science writer explains that "mental stimulation, in the long run, is more essential to the body than food."

Kotulak means that in order to keep your three-pound master organ in proper working order, you have to constantly challenge it. Kotulak even says, "It is education that is emerging as the most critical predictor of longevity and health." Therefore, as soon as you finish this piece, push aside all your other chores and responsibilities and do at least one of the following:

1. Buy tickets to the symphony, or find a free play or other cultural event. You hate the ballet, right? Well, one time won't kill you.

2. Join an explorers club, or renew your membership in an alumni group or association.

3. Visit your library and check out a serious book you've been meaning to read for years. Consider *War and Peace* by Leo Tolstoy or *Common Ground* by the late J. Anthony Lukas.

4. Vow to take up crossword or jigsaw puzzles or perhaps bridge.

5. Here's a tough task: learn a foreign language.

6. Take up a musical instrument.

Keep in mind the key component to saving your memory is to find new activities. Break out of your routine. Seek new challenges in order to stimulate brain cell activity. These cells need the provocation in order to function. Undoubtedly you've read it before—the brain is like a muscle and, like muscles, it must be worked. Use it, brother, or lose it. Or as the world-renowned conductor Arthur Fiedler once said, "If you stop, you rot."

As the result of experimentation, we now know the brain is susceptible to stimulation. Kotulak notes, "The most important discovery for me was that the brain gets better and better through exercise but 'rusts' with disuse, placing the ability to build brain power squarely into the hands of each one of us." As a researcher based in California told Kotulak, "People don't realize the power they have within themselves to change their brains." ◆

# CHAPTER SEVEN

# *Being Creative,*

## *NOW!*

*"The creative person is both more primitive
and more cultivated. . . a lot madder and a
lot saner, than the average person."*

—Frank Barron

*"Man's main task in life
is to give birth to himself."*

—Erich Fromm

I t is Monday morning, the beginning of your sixth week in retirement. You have no idea what you're going to do with the long day that stretches ahead of you. Hey, it's time to discover something entirely new. You decide to get creative. But how? Where do you begin?

If I could, I would send you to Washington, D.C., to meet Gene Cohen. One of Dr. Cohen's special interests is creativity in aging. "What is considerably overlooked, if not denied," he maintains, "is the opportunity and frequency of creative growth and expression among older adults."

Cohen told this story to drive his point home. When the Corcoran Museum of Art in Washington exhibited the works of folk artists in a retrospective covering the years 1930–1980, he discovered that of the twenty artists in the exhibit, sixteen were 65 years or older—and they were the new kids on the block. Of those sixteen, six of the artists were at least 80.

In a paper for the *American Journal of Geriatric Psychiatry,* Cohen wrote, "Most of these artists had only begun their work, or first reached their mature phase, after age 65. Bill Traylor, whose work was featured on the cover of the exhibit catalog, had been born a slave. He created his first painting at the age of 85.

"Folk art is dominated by older artists," Cohen explained. "Grandma Moses, for example, began painting at age 78. That an entire field of art should be dominated by older artists argues these individuals cannot be stereotypically dismissed as outliers or *Ripley's Believe It Or Not* cases—creative potential in later life resides not just with the Picassos, but with a broad range of individuals."

Creativity, of course, means different things to different people. To the average person, creativity might be defined as a rare gift, something only a privileged few—poets, musicians, authors, painters, researchers, rocket scientists—possess. Horse feathers! Creativity is a state of mind, a way of looking at life and its tasks. In other words, everyone has the potential to be creative and probably is, though they don't recognize it.

"Creativity is an approach to solving problems," Yale psychologist Robert Sternberg told *New Choices* magazine. "It's a frame of mind whose principles apply to every aspect of life. Living and working more imaginatively is a joy in itself."

When you're being creative, you approach your day and its

challenges in a way that allows you to see them as fresh and interesting rather than familiar and tedious. You can apply your creativity to the writing of a letter to a grandchild, to fixing a special meal for an anniversary, to finding a way to make your swimming workout spirited as well as tiring.

Authors Connie Goldman and Richard Mahler, in their *Secrets of Becoming a Late Bloomer,* quote ceramic artist Beatrice Wood as saying, "One can be creative wherever one is. Creative persons are those who are open to life and listening to life as it comes to them. You can be creative inside even as you're washing the dishes."

Let's say you want to learn new things, but you feel hesitant, unsure of your capacity for new undertakings. If that's the case, you need to get in touch with what psychologists call your inner self. Author Eda LeShan tells us that "Middle age is the time for men to think about what is on the inside, rather than the outside."

For those who are not self-starters, there are any number of places to begin the quest. Take a short course of your choosing, either at a community college, a YMCA, or a senior university. For example, in Chicago there is a course called "The Artist's Way: A Course in Creative Recovery," taught by Phyllis Estes Cady. This lady does not subscribe to the idea that older adults are not creative. "These seniors say to me, 'I'm just not creative.' Or even worse, 'I was creative once. But I've lost it.' That's non-sense," she said, emphatically. "There is an artist inside all of us. Further, we become creative by asking for help.

"It sounds contradictory, but it's not. I know it isn't easy to ask for help, and it gets harder the older we get. It's very humbling to think of ourselves as rank beginners at 60, 70, or 80. But what a vibrancy this brings us," Cady said. "What is more inspiring than an octogenarian freshman? Look in your local newspaper and sign up for a beginner's drawing class. Or a writing class. Take some risk. Don't deprive yourself of the joy of being a beginner. Creativity begins anew every day."

To help you get in the mood and move you off square one, I offer the Outrageous Older Man's list of ways to begin your new life as a Creative Person.

1. Make a list of twenty things you truly enjoy doing. Then, go do them.

2. Make a list of ten books that you've wanted to read. Go to the library and start checking them out.

3. Make a list of twenty places you'd like to visit in and around your community. Next, plan your day-trips and begin your tours. Include your wife or a close friend.

4. Make a list of interesting people you'd like to meet in your community. Phone them up, one at a time, and offer to volunteer at one of their projects for an afternoon. You may be pleasantly surprised at the responses.

5. Now accept this assignment: turn to the next chapter (after you've finished this one), and learn a little bit about writing as an avocation. Then flip over to Chapter Fifteen and read about the efficacy of change.

I understand this creativity business can be intimidating when you're first starting out, so here's a personal experience that might prove reassuring. I was in Chicago several years ago, attending the American Society on Aging's annual meeting, and searching for something offbeat to feature in my column. I found a session called "Storytelling—The Very Heart of Life" and decided to attend.

An hour later, I found myself trying to hide in my seat toward the back of the classroom. I felt entirely out of place. Here I was, a white-haired man with a press pass surrounded by twenty-nine very attentive young and middle-aged women. At the front of the room, an instructor was saying, "These will be sacred stories.

Therefore, this is a sacred place." Then she lit a stubby white candle, referring to it as the candle of wisdom. She announced that the participants, "including our gentleman visitor, who is welcome here," would break into groups of five or six and form circles of storytellers.

I was trapped, cornered inside a course subtitled "The Heroine's Journey to Storytelling," a description that I had somehow overlooked. Over the next ninety uncomfortable minutes, one after another of the women in our group told a very personal and moving story. (In tears, one woman recounted how she was born an illegitimate child.) The rest of us encouraged and supported each storyteller.

At the conclusion, we all gathered in a large circle, holding hands and our instructor, Jacqueline Tobin of the University of Denver, summarized, "In our culture, a woman's journey has been a solitary one. Telling our stories allows us, individually, collectively, and across generations, to have the courage to undertake our journeys. We find our way and return to claim our power. Thereafter, we recognize that through it all, we are not alone."

I walked away from the session thinking, "I'm glad I wandered in. Those women are okay." Besides, I got a good column out of the experience. Much later, I concluded that all of us are comfort creatures. We want to stay where it's familiar, comfortable, unchallenging. The Buddhists teach, "If you want to change your kharma, change your surroundings." Men, much more than women, find it easy to put themselves into a comfort-box as they age. Over time, the box gets smaller and smaller. Then creativity is precluded and becomes beyond reach.

Wherever you are—retired or in the workplace—don't let yourself be boxed in. Suzanne Merrit is the founder of the Creativity and Innovation Laboratory at Polaroid's headquarters in Cambridge, MA. Here, employees are taught a range of new and creative approaches to problem solving. She says, "What we've found is that creativity is almost like physical conditioning. We need to exercise it."

That's fair. I'll add the following point made by Gene Cohen about physician and poet William Carlos Williams. "In his 60s, Williams suffered a stroke and subsequent severe depression. These blows ended his medical practice. But he emerged from loss to write some of his best poetry, including work at age 79 that led to a Pulitzer prize."

Cohen adds that in his last years, Williams wrote about "an old age that adds as it takes away." Thus the poet-healer makes manifest "the human capacity to mobilize creative responses to crisis throughout the life cycle."

The successful life is one of continual growth and expansion. In the end, we are invited to become men who understand that all of life is a quest. The goal is to be the very best that we can be.

# CHAPTER EIGHT

# Write It,

## OUTRAGEOUSLY

*"A professional writer
is an amateur who didn't quit."*

—Richard Bach

"**Y**ou cannot figure readers," read the lead sentence to one of my columns several years back. "At this very moment, two women are mad as wet hens because I previously suggested, in forceful, no-nonsense language, that freelance writing is no way to earn a livelihood, particularly in your retirement years."

I was, of course, speaking out of my own experience. Moreover, I felt my opinion reflected the marketplace. Consider that in 1967, when I left the *Saturday Evening Post*, my article price was a respectable $2,500. In the thirty-one years since that heady time, no publication has ever matched that sum. Most freelance writers I know have either working spouses or some additional source of income. My pal Ralph Schoenstein, who has ghosted all of Bill Cosby's books and endures as a freelance author, says he still meets neighbors who begin each conversation with "Are you still writing? Or have you taken a job?"

However, the economics do not matter to the protesting woman who set me straight. "Why would you tell a retiree there is no future in freelancing if that is what he has his heart set on?" Sue Curry, of Bowling Green, KY, wanted to know. "I am one of those who didn't begin writing for the public until I was 52. Before that, I raised a family. . . I always kept a diary though, and hoped the day would come when I could devote my full time to writing. Well, I have realized my dream. . . and the personal satisfaction of seeing my name in print beats all the wealth in the world."

I no longer try to dissuade wannabe writers. To the contrary, I encourage them, believing that memoir writing and similar writing pursuits constitute a form of therapy. Moreover, it's a trend, a movement, a veritable force unto itself. The newspaper published by the American Association of Retired Persons recently reported that memoir writing "is a pastime that has taken the country by storm."

I can vouch for that. In one of my columns, I volunteered to critique freelance pieces. More than seventy of them arrived in no time, including two self-published books. I responded to every last submission and used two of them—both strong, well-crafted personal narratives—in subsequent columns.

Meanwhile, under a headline reading "Older Writers Budding and Blossoming," *The New York Times* reported, "Here in the city of Wharton and Mailer, where literary yearnings flourish and fade, there is a subspecies of struggling writer for whom the dream doesn't die and the struggle rolls on into old age. These writers defy the stereotype. . . Their turf is the senior centers; Social Security sustains them."

Reporter Janny Scott wrote, "All over New York City, men and women in their 70s, 80s, and 90s turn up at writing classes. . . trying to be published at an age when they might be expected to have given up." The article, which began on page one, quoted a playwright and writing teacher who said of his elderly students, "Their writing gives them a certain youthfulness. I fully believe that writing has kept a lot of these people alive."

"Storytelling is the enduring expression of the human spirit," said the late philanthropist/entrepreneur Maury P. Leibovitz, who left money enough to support the Legacies true story contest. Leibovitz, a psychologist and teacher who died in 1992, preached that everyone has a story to tell, and older adults should feel that someone has listened to them.

The nonprofit Leibovitz Foundation, with the help of the Jewish Association for Services for the Aged in New York, recently completed its fourth nonfiction contest, awarding fifty-three cash prizes totaling $15,000. Since 1991, more than 36,000 men and women, all 60 and older, have competed in these free contests.

One summer I interviewed the winner of the third Legacies contest and wrote, "There is a biblical quality to the prize-winning story that Stan Cohen tells. Essentially it is—do a good deed, and it will return to you, a thousand-fold."

Cohen, then 63, is a Korean War veteran who was born in Brooklyn but now lives in Huntington Beach, CA. His story reached back to a time when, as a young man, he worked for the Internal Revenue Service. He was a brand new collections officer sent to confront a thin, unshaven elderly man, a widower of 77 who was in a wheelchair. The man, Hector Fernandez, owed the IRS $25,000.

"I've been expecting you," Fernandez said to agent Cohen. "I would like to tell you a little story," he added, after first serving his guest a cup of instant coffee. The story was this:

Fernandez was entitled to a $200 refund. In error, the IRS mailed him a $25,000 check. Hector Fernandez returned the money twice. The IRS repeated the mistake, and then the little man who had dreamed all his adult life of traveling decided to take a cruise. As Cohen listened, Fernandez rationalized and then rhapsodized over his misadventure.

"I'm an old man, I'm in a wheelchair and I don't feel so good," Fernandez began. "If I went to jail, I probably wouldn't live too long. I decided, then and there, to spend that $25,000!" So he bought a first class ticket to sail around the world, sixty-five glorious days on the Queen Elizabeth II, making port in Hawaii, Tahiti, Fiji, Tokyo, Bangkok, Indonesia, Calcutta, Israel, Egypt, France, England, New York, Florida, through the Panama Canal, and home to Los Angeles.

"It was a fairy tale come true," said the aged invalid. "For the first and only time in my life, I was treated like a king. Why, I even had a steward assigned to take me places and show me everything."

When the long story was ended, the little man in the wheelchair began to weep. "I am ready now to go to jail," he murmured. "Take me, sir," and with that he held out his bony wrists, expecting to have handcuffs snapped onto them.

Instead, Stan Cohen left quietly. Back in his office he dictated a brief report which effectively closed the case. He wrote the initials UTL on the file: "Unable To Locate." His narrative, incidentally, was entitled "Confessions of a Tax Collector."

In our telephone interview, Stan Cohen was giddy, reflective and, above all, undeniably happy. "It's the first story I ever wrote," he confessed, explaining that unknown to him, a publisher in Huntington Beach had sent his piece to the Legacies contest. "I'm thrilled," he repeated. "I'm having so much fun over this deal."

When I had cranked out the Legacies column, the third or fourth time I had visited the subject, I again concluded that seniors who write are all winners, no matter what the contest results tell them. Why, even the American Psychological Association confirms the writing experience can result in better physical and mental health.

Many senior writers are *good,* far better than I once believed.

If you doubt this statement, I challenge you to buy or borrow the book *Legacies*. Following the first contest, the sponsors chose 162 of the best pieces and turned them into this largely unheralded, modest-selling book. A paperback edition followed a year later.

Finally, there are the voices of the writers themselves, explaining how they are taller, richer, younger, more robust, more articulate, prouder, more confident and energetic—all because they forced themselves to write and emote, testing their long-neglected talents.

"Now that my social status has been elevated from gabby old coot to raconteur, I waddle a little prouder," states a New York contestant. A Connecticut man says, "You ask how the writing of my story affected me. Is the sky blue? Do the birds sing? Absolutely, and my writing has affected all of my being. I practically wake up smiling, ready for any challenge to come along."

If you believe you must write—if you truly have a story you want your grandchildren to know, or you feel compelled to write your way past a sadness—then let nothing dissuade you, not even the prospect of being poorly and unfairly paid for your words.

If you want to write, consider entering the next Legacies contest. Writers must be 60 years or older and their stories may not exceed 1,500 words. They should be typed on 8½" x 11" paper. Be certain to include your name, date of birth, address and telephone number at the top of your story. Only one true story per entrant.

Mail your manuscript to National Legacies Contest, 163 Amsterdam Avenue Box 107, New York, NY 10023. For further information, phone (800) 561-9024. ◆

# CHAPTER NINE

# Rx for Aging:

## LAUGHTER IN DAILY DOSES

*"Of all the gifts bestowed by nature
on human beings, hearty laughter
must be close to the top."*

—Norman Cousins,
*Head First: The Biology of Hope*

There were nine white-haired women along with five of us thick-waisted men in the classroom, all students at Elder Camp, a program run by the Canyon Ranch people in the Berkshire Mountains of Massachusetts. We were going back to school for ten days to learn about successful aging. Each student carried a thick loose-leaf notebook that contained this definition:

"Successful aging means that we need not see ourselves as victims of the whims of disabling diseases, which may have once characterized our understanding of aging. A very important element in our quest is keeping an open mind. . . we must also remember there are numerous health teachers."

Into the classroom walked a short, stocky lecturer, wearing Groucho glasses with a false nose that, while large and outsized, seemed to be the exact replica of his God-given nose. The program warned us this class was to be about humor, and the star of our show was Israel "Izzy" Gesell, a 30-something fellow who introduced himself as an American humorologist.

"I want you to take life seriously, but yourselves lightly," he began. "Stress is not an event, it's our perception of an event. Therefore, the way to deal with stress is to alter our perception.

"Humor is an underutilized resource for most people," he continued. "As we become adults we're told to be serious, to straighten up. Right now, I need you to turn a switch in your minds. Smile! Put on a happy face. Remember, a pleasurable memory is as real to the body as the original event."

Izzy Gesell looked into our faces. Our senior member was older than 80, the youngest a baby of 62. "You are the custodians of what humor used to be," he said next. "Your humor is a wistful humor, about what courtship used to be, of struggling to make a living, of relatives who came too often and stayed too long. Don't let your humor disappear or be forgotten. Be funny for your grandchildren. Also, be funny for yourself, for the sake of your good health."

It was the great Russian novelist Fyodor Dostoyevsky (1821–1881) who wrote, "If you wish to glimpse inside a human soul and get to know a man, you'll get better results if you just watch him laugh. If he laughs well, he's a good man." The late Norman Cousins—editor, author, and teacher—persuaded millions of Americans that laughter, along with the will of the patient, represents a powerful key to wellness. In a celebrated case, Cousins, then the editor of the *Saturday Review of Literature* in New York, helped cure himself of painful ankylosing spondylitis (a form of arthritis in the spine) using laughter as a tonic, a pain reliever.

His 1976 best-seller *Anatomy of an Illness* told how he watched funny movies for the express purpose of inducing hearty laughter. He later wrote, "Ten minutes of solid belly laughter would give me two hours of painfree sleep." Cousins firmly believed, and taught students in medical school, that laughter stimulates and activates endorphins, hormones known as the body's own morphine. Thus the intellectual Cousins, who was the author of twenty books and held an honorary degree in medicine from Yale University, put his stamp of approval on the healthful benefits of the human behavior we know as laughter.

Dr. William Fry, professor emeritus at Stanford University and a veteran researcher of laughter, has said that laughing 100 times a day would be the equivalent of 10 minutes of exercise on a rowing machine. This psychiatrist explains that laughter reduces pain perception and stimulates the production of hormones. The hormones, in their turn, increase blood flow, and the whole process strengthens the immune system. And, as everyone knows, laughter is a stress-buster.

As a newspaper columnist, I am often asked whether I believe that the older adults who know how to laugh and have fun will live longer than the cranks, grouches, and spoilsports who give aging a bad name. My answer goes like this: "Never let the child inside you grow up or die. Keep your party hat close by, always."

Another committed disciple of senior fun is anthropologist and author Ashley Montagu. He teaches that "The truth about the human species is that we are intended to remain in many ways childlike; we were never intended to grow up."

A child laughs 250 times a day on average, while an adult laughs just fifteen times in every twenty-four hours. The evidence, I submit, is overwhelming. We adults are obviously neglecting our sense of humor and consequently are depriving ourselves of significant, life-affirming experiences.

I once put all this philosophy and expertise to a test. I paid a visit to south Miami where two of my favorite children live—

granddaughters Melissa Adele Lindeman (ten years old as I write this), and Stephanie (age 6 going on 10). Stephanie is a chronologically-challenged child whose middle name is "Keepin' Up." Both are redheads and both accept that Grandpa Bard is ancient, yet good fun in the swimming pool. Jumping on his head is among their favorite tricks.

When these two open their cute little mouths, there's no telling what will spill out. Once, seeing me beside my much-younger wife, Melissa earnestly asked, "Are you guys *really* married?" On that same visit several years ago, she watched me, bare-chested in the pool, and commented, "Grandpa Bard, you have boobies."

This trip, I checked into my hotel in Coral Gables and in the early evening the kids arrived for some serious, protracted swim activities. Now self-conscious about my torso, I kept my tank top on until the last possible moment. Several hundred cannonballs later—I refer to the knees-first children's dive guaranteed to send up a large splash—we dried off and headed for cheeseburgers. Later, we retired to my room where, with absolutely no warning, a raucous, shriek-filled game of hide-and-seek broke out.

Childlike imagination, stamina, and a lust for laughter and squeals overflowed room 509 in the historic, stately Biltmore Hotel. Even though there are only four possible places to hide in any hotel room—the shower, the closet, under the bed, behind the drapes—the game went on and on for 45 minutes. I was in awe of their determination to amuse themselves and good old Grandpa Bard, as well. My sides actually hurt from their contagious laughter.

The growing child and the older man have certain things in common. In both cases, the desire for love and the search for laughter are among their more evident yearnings. This I believe.

# THE
# *Outrageous*
# BODY

# CHAPTER TEN

# Take Charge

## OF YOUR HEALTH, CAPTAIN

*"If I'd spent as much time and effort taking care of my body as I've done my cars, I'd be a lot healthier."*

—a retired steelworker named Al, in a letter to the American Association of Retired Persons

Because the issue we know as health is so immense—encyclopedic, in fact—I will begin with an anecdote. Hopefully, this short, personal narrative may serve as a larger object lesson.

The youthful, good-looking orthopedic surgeon swept into the examining room, lifted my leg by the ankle and, almost at once said, "We can scope this out. You'll be fine." He directed me to have a sophisticated X-ray of the heel called a CAT scan (computerized axial tomography) and, thereafter, to phone his secretary to make a date for surgery.

Holy Toledo and just a minute, Doctor Quick-to-Cut! My problem was in my heel, or more accurately, the Achilles tendon running into the heel. It was painful. It was also swollen, stiff as a board and, on occasion, hot to the touch, all of which meant walking was a big problem. Jogging, jumping rope, and even slow biking were out of the question.

My self-diagnosis had been "inflamed tendon," the result of overuse; quite possibly, the problem was compounded by age. (I was 66 at the time.) Friends assured me that I was not alone in my misery. "Yeah, I had mine two years," one friend told me. "Takes forever to heal."

My first telephone call upon leaving the sports medicine clinic was to Dr. Paul Lindeman, my son, the emergency-room physician and board-certified internist. "What did he mean he was going to scope it out?" Dr. Paul asked. I had no idea. I did know, however, that I wasn't ready for ankle surgery followed by a long rehabilitation period.

Instead, I decided to take to the backyard swimming pool where, each late afternoon, I walked back and forth, lifting my bad ankle upward in waist-high water. I did this fifty, sixty, seventy times, spending upwards of 45 minutes at this home-based therapy each day. I also worked on dry land, leaning up against any wall I could find where, putting one foot in front of the other, I stretched.

After a summer of exercise, I pronounced myself healed. Gone were the soreness, the inflammation and swelling. I had saved the Medicare program hundreds of dollars, and myself from the trauma and possible poor result of surgery.

My experience, however, amounts to a sample of one. It's nothing more than a story with a happy ending. It lacks scientific evidence or conclusions, meaning you cannot treat your Achilles tendonitis as I did and expect the same results. Nonetheless, I stand behind this injunction: do not meekly or blindly submit to surgery simply because some doctor wants to operate on you. Bear in mind, please, what Albert Schweitzer and other wise men of science have taught: *you are your own best doctor.*

You are forewarned. You must accept responsibility for your body and your overall health, and be the captain of your health-care team, for no one is going to take better care of you than you are. Interview, read, experiment (with prudence!) and don't hesitate to seek out a second, even a third, medical opinion.

For the greatest part of my professional life, I've been involved in health or medical reporting. In 1970, I became the editor-in-chief of *Today's Health* magazine and worked out of American Medical Association's headquarters, a place sometimes referred to as "the House of Medicine." Following the death of my first wife, a death we Lindemans believed could be traced to medical negligence, I told my three children that we could spend our lives hating medicine for what it did to us or "we can do our utmost to make medicine better—both as science and as an art." To that end, I would continue as a health reporter and interpreter for consumers, and when Paul, the independent middle child, showed a keen interest in science, I hoped he might become a doctor. First I helped him get a job as a surgical orderly then as a research aide in a laboratory. One night over dinner he announced, "Dad, I think I'll go to medical school." I recall the moment as though it were yesterday.

In Miami, I covered thirty-five hospitals. It was a bad day when I wasn't inside some clinic or ward interviewing doctors, nurses, patients. Then, at *50 Plus* magazine, I had two excellent teaching doctors writing regularly for our readers. The first was the late William A. Nolen, author of *The Making of a Surgeon,* and the second was Edward A. Rosenbaum, author of *A Taste of My Own Medicine.*

Does all this make me an expert, a guru for older men? Of course not! Should you listen to me rather than your doctor? A thousand times no. However, I did learn a thing or three, and here, from the heart, is my best advice.

Again and again throughout the years on my beat, I heard bright, opinionated doctors philosophize that "the next great revolution in medicine will take place when the American consumer accepts responsibility for his (or her) own health."

Consider the following scenario: the average Joe of 50, 60, even 70, eats red meat (which is very high in fat content), insists on desserts, drinks two beers or wine with his meals, and gets no exercise on a regular basis. What's more, he works eight to ten hours a day, sleeps fitfully, slugs down antacid medicine, and watches sports on television as though his life depended on it. At the first sign of trouble—a pain in his chest, for instance—he speeds to the nearest clinic imploring, "You've got to do something, Doc. Give me medicine, pills, something. Make me well. That's your job, isn't it?"

My response to this question may strike you as outrageous, but it remains, "No, it isn't." More often than not, you make yourself sick. Then, if you're fortunate and blessed, you make yourself well. The medical practitioners are your guides. They are there to listen, to diagnose, to suggest, and yes, to prescribe. But the real healing happens between the doctor and patient. Together, you and your doctors call upon your body's (and mind's) natural healing system.

Writer and physician Mike Oppenheim said it best. "The average family doctor cures no more than 10 to 20 percent of the patients he or she sees. Most common complaints (viral infections, upset stomachs, strains, sprains, other minor injuries) are self-limited. They go away on their own. And many serious illnesses (diabetes, high blood pressure, or heart disease) are managed and controlled, but never cured."

According to Oppenheim, "Your doctor sometimes can work miracles, but most of the time he can't. If you know very little about your body and the illnesses that can afflict it, he can supply the knowledge. But if you're willing to learn, you can supply the knowledge yourself. So learn. Read a book!"

In his book *Fifty to Forever*, Hugh Downs, the television reporter and host, wrote that, "YOU are the key to maintaining your health throughout your life. I'm not advocating disrespect or anarchy," he explained. "Most doctors understand this. They know that ultimately, you must act while they advise."

To help you take charge of your own health care, here are ten common sense rules to follow. You have my word that obedience to them will help you gain admission to the Outrageous Older Men's Health & Fitness Club.

1. Accept that you are the captain of your health team. Act accordingly. Don't be intimidated by your doctors. Speak out—they're busy so you need to make them spend time answering your questions.

2. Do not smoke. Avoid secondhand cigarette smoke and wherever possible, campaign against smoking. Forgive me, but I am a zealot on this subject. You see, I watched my late mother waste away day after day, a victim of emphysema and lung cancer. It is a powerful lesson that lasts a lifetime. And if you are a grandparent, you have a duty to preach to those grandkids about the terrible consequences of tobacco addiction.

3. Exercise. Begin, please, by reading and taking to heart the words in Chapter Thirteen of this book.

4. Be a nut about nutrition. It's a new, emerging science undergoing an information explosion. So read, study, be conservative. Meantime, go for the fruits and vegetables, five servings a day, at least.

5. Be positive. Take strength from the fact that while we're surrounded and immersed in melancholy news about diseases, syndromes, and maladies, we older Americans are living longer and stronger. Disabilities among the elderly have declined 14.5 percent since 1982, confounding the doomsayers. According to Richard Suzman of the National Institute on Aging, "Not only are there fewer disabled people, those who are disabled seem to have fewer disabilities."

6. Sure, take extra care of your automobile, but scuttle the stoicism about your body. I want you to be in charge. I also want you to take advantage of good medicine. Get your regular checkups and when it's time to consult a doctor, be a self-starter. I'm referring now to the monitoring of your blood pressure and heart health. Be conscientious about colorectal exams, melanoma screening, eye exams, dental checkups, and immunizations. Flu shots are Medicare approved, remember. Polls show that one-third of American men haven't seen a doctor in the past twelve months, while 10 percent admitted they hadn't been inside a doctor's examining room in five years. That's inexcusable for allegedly grown men. Our aging bodies need and deserve the best possible care.

7. We've both lived too long and heard too much long-winded advice on alcohol. Two words sum up all the wisdom: drink responsibly. Simply put, alcohol is toxic.

8. If you're a widower or single, you may want to consider marrying. Studies at the University of California and Princeton University show that unmarried men have higher illness rates and die earlier than their married peers. One reason that marriage may promote better health is that partners help us cope with stress.

9. Take your health seriously, but yourself lightly. Laugh at your pranks and pratfalls, and laugh at the goofy world around you. According to Dr. Raymond Flannery, Jr., of Harvard Medical School, as many as 75 percent of all doctor's visits are due to stress-related illnesses. As we said in a previous chapter, humor is a stress buster. In other words, laughter can equal wellness.

10. At the risk of sounding like the *Reader's Digest,* I'll pass on the findings of a report described in the international *Journal of Psychiatry in Medicine.* It showed that older people (age 65 and up) who attended church services once a week had stronger immune systems. The scientists speculated that feelings of belonging, of togetherness, even of worship, helped the body to cope. This outcome once more supports the body-mind connection and points to the fact that a commitment to a higher authority, amplified by the power of prayer, can affect individual health positively. "There's no question that religious faith can help people get better," states Dr. Dale A. Matthews of Georgetown University Medical School and the National Institute for Healthcare Research.

"Old men should be explorers," wrote T.S. Eliot. Yes, they should be explorers in search of their own best possible health. It's a task for a lifetime.

# What Really Kills Us

Two leading scientists, Doctors J. Michael McGinnis and William Foege, analyzed sixteen years of published research in order to determine the "external factors" leading to the death of two million American men and women every year. The results: the investigators estimate half of all deaths in the United States can be attributed to the following root causes, and thus may be considered premature.

| | |
|---|---|
| Tobacco | 400,000 |
| Diet and activity level | 300,000 |
| Alcohol | 100,000 |
| Infectious agents | 90,000 |
| Toxic agents | 60,000 |
| Firearms | 35,000 |
| Sexual behavior | 30,000 |
| Motor vehicles | 25,000 |
| Illicit drug use | 20,000 |

# CHAPTER ELEVEN

# Living Longer

## . . . BETTER, TOO

*"I shall die young,
at whatever age the experience occurs."*

—Ruth Bernard, on contemplating her 80th
birthday which she intended to spend
climbing Mt. Fuji in Japan (elevation 12,388
feet), quoted in a publication of the
American Association of Retired Persons

The study of extended life spans has moved beyond the realm of science fiction until it has become one of research's hot new areas. A direct result of this is that people of considerable intelligence now say one day we shall see marathoners who are 106 and writers of novels who are 120; aging is not inevitable; people can reach seniorhood and still maintain themselves as healthy and productive.

Dr. Kenneth Cooper, considered the father of aerobics and founder of the Cooper Aerobics Center in Dallas, declares, "We're eventually going to rewrite all the textbooks on aging."

The point is that older adults are being told, again and again, if we eat right, exercise right, we can postpone disease and dependency until past 85, even 90. Then (coming soon!) medical science will produce a wonder drug (or combination of drugs) to stop the aging clock. After all, in laboratories around the world, some of the brightest scientific investigators are exploring the efficacy of thousands of substances, from antioxidants, to melatonin, hormone replacement therapy, and the intriguing hormonal precursor DHEA. Their goal: to halt senescence—and they vow it will happen. It's just a question of putting more pedal to the metal.

Well, I'm not going to hold my breath waiting. The wisest thing you and I can do for the moment is to disabuse ourselves of the widely held American notion that one magical pill is going to halt aging, and even replace it with youth and vigor. Instead, I suggest we remind each other that the process we know as "growing old" is enormously complicated. Some scientists believe it will never be fully understood.

Having said this, I feel compelled now to deliver encouraging capsule reports from the front lines of longevity research. We begin with molecular biologist Tom H. Johnson of the University of Colorado, who is something of an outrageous researcher. In 1995, he told the *Harvard Health Letter,* "If we don't blow ourselves up or kill ourselves in toxic soup, we may dramatically extend the [human] life span."

Researcher Johnson is certainly doing his part for longevity. He has succeeded in keeping tiny worms (*Caenorhabditias elegans*) alive long beyond their normal span. Other investigators, meanwhile, have extended life for fruit flies, yeast, rodents, primates. These life-extenders believe that what works in the laboratory on lower forms will some day work in humans. Johnson's technique was to isolate a gene (age-1) which enables normal cells to withstand environmental stresses, such as heat, radiation, and a toxic herbicide.

Now consider the possibilities here. Say that we discover and isolate a human gene that strengthens normal cells, making them invulnerable to the stresses of everyday wear and tear. Couldn't these genetically-altered, reinforced cells then prove to be ageless? Plainly, where the science of longevity is concerned, new rules are being written and giving rise to talk of doubling or tripling life expectancy.

"Until recently, most scientists thought extension of the life span was impossible," says Dr. Richard Cutler of the National Institute on Aging. "The problem is that such studies have been plagued by thousands of years of quackery. But mental blocks against anti-aging are slowly being challenged."

While we wait for discoveries enabling us to extend our life span, there remains plenty for us to do to thwart the infirmities that accompany aging. No one wants to hear these injunctions, though, for they have to do with getting plenty of exercise, living by a prudent diet, and having a socially active lifestyle. (You'll find lots of good advice on these subjects in Chapters Ten and Thirteen.)

"Aging is really much more within our grasp than we might think," Dr. Jeanne Wei of Harvard Medical School sums up. But "Even if we identify the longevity-relevant gene or genes, they will not significantly help people who don't take care of themselves." Almost every authority on the subject agrees that no pill can ever substitute for the benefits of good nutrition complemented by exercise.

Let's now turn to America's centenarians, those oldsters who have managed—on their own—to live 100 years and beyond. In the land that worships youth, these super-old or old-old people are among the media's new favorites because along with their outrageous opinions, these 100-plus folks are making news. Consider that in 1960 there were just 3,000 of these survivors. At present, there are 59,000 advanced-in-age senior men and women, according to the Census Bureau. By the year 2050, however, there will be one million centenarians who, as a specific age-cohort, are among the fastest-growing segments of the population.

Dan Georgakas, author of *The Methuselah Factors,* says, "We appear to be on the brink of a longevity breakthrough in which a hundredth birthday will cease to be of note." Well, there is already some proof of that. Willard Scott, of the *Today Show* (MSNBC/TV), can no longer honor all requests for a broadcast salute on that special 100th birthday because he gets more than 400 of these a week.

Although I never met him, my favorite centenarian was Sidney Amber, a Californian, and at 109 the oldest United States citizen to receive Social Security—and the oldest American to still pay into the system. Yes, Amber was working at 109. On weekends he held court in a restaurant where he served as a host, always ready with a quip, a handshake, or a grin for a souvenir photo. I am indebted to my friend Paul Kleyman of the American Society on Aging for introducing me to Amber. In the newspaper he edits for the society, Kleyman wrote about Sidney Amber's 109th birthday.

"Do you feel as good as you look?" he asked.

Amber replied, "Today, I feel better than I look." Kleyman then described how Amber "blew out every one of the 109 candles with one breath."

Following his birthday, Amber appeared on Jay Leno's *Tonight Show* along with comic Jonathan Winters. After some small talk and laughs about being 109, Winters remarked, "I don't know if I could see 109."

Amber was ready for him. "You may not see it," he shot back, "but you still might get there."

So might we all.

# Prevalent Myths About Aging That Deserve Your Scorn

*"A human being would certainly not grow to be 70 or 80 years old if this longevity had no meaning for the species. The afternoon of human life must also have a significance of its own and cannot be merely a pitiful appendage to life's morning."*
—Carl Jung

Myth: Members of the 65-plus crowd are all unhealthy.
**Fact: Almost every study concludes the greatest majority of those 65 and older consider themselves capable of doing whatever they want.**

Myth: Older people live in the past. Life passes them by.
**Fact: Senior men and women read more than any other age group and enthusiastically support and fund this country's performing arts. City symphonies and museums would shut down without their older patrons. Does this sound as though modern life is too much for the expanding legions of successful agers?**

Myth: Old people lose their sexual attractiveness.
**Fact: Look around you in restaurants, theaters, concert halls, museums, sporting events, and senior centers. You'll spot men and women in their maturity who are well-dressed, glamorous, sensual, and sexy.**

Myth: Old people are all alike.

**Fact: People actually become less alike as they age. We're referring to more than 30 million people here. How can anyone believe that many people are all alike? I ask you, are golfer Chi Chi Rodriguez and former president George Bush alike? How about feminist Gloria Steinem and singer Rosemary Clooney? Peas in a pod? Not hardly.**

Myth: The terms "old" and "needy" mean the same thing.

**Fact: An estimated 80 percent of all the money in savings and loans is held by those older than 50.** ◆

# How Long Do You Want to Live?

If you're like most senior adults, you want to live as long as your life is good. . . as long as you're active, independent, and in command of your senses. Then, tucked away in a small corner of your consciousness is a very special wish. You wish to see a granddaughter marry and start a family, cancer cured, your Home Depot stock split, the Cubs get into a World Series, the United States establish a colony on the moon.

With these thoughts in mind, you're eager to learn more about longevity—and you're not especially discriminating about the source of this alleged news. Admit it, you're a sucker for every new vitamin, herb, supplement. If it's labeled "wonder drug," you give it a long look.

Please remember the golden rule for the health consumer—if it looks too good to be true, it probably is. So keep your money in your pocket. To help you separate the bogus from the *bona fide,* here are seven rules to keep in mind as you read through your newspapers, newsletters, and magazines.

1. Don't jump to conclusions. Changing your daily habits on the basis of a single study is never a good idea.

2. Keep your natural skepticism in good working order. Authentic breakthroughs rarely happen, yet that word remains a favorite with most journalists. The discovery of penicillin and the polio vaccine were breakthroughs. Today that word is so overworked, it is meaningless.

3. Notice where the information is coming from. What authorities are cited? Does the writer rely on scientific evidence or anecdotes? Is a medical journal quoted or cited? Remember that the *New England Journal of Medicine, Lancet* (a British journal), and the *Journal of the American Medical Association* are three of the most prestigious sources of information about medicine and health. Jane Brody's personal health columns in *The New York Times* are thorough and well researched.

4. Use common sense and apply logic. If the writer says the Japanese are healthier than Americans because they eat fish, stop and think. The Japanese also eat a lot of rice. Does the writer go on to prove to your satisfaction that fish in the Japanese diet is the one—and only—reason for their general good health?

5. Be wary when studies are cited to promote a commercial product. Does the writer mention that company's stock? Did the stock fluctuate because of the announcement?

6. Try to distinguish between "promising advances" and public health recommendations. For example, if a medical

team performs a successful heart and lung transplant, that's interesting. But what does it mean to the average person? If, however, the Surgeon General states that cigarette smoking is a cause of lung cancer, you can assume that many studies support his recommendations not to smoke.

7. Make no changes in your health regimen without a good deal of reading, study, and at least one conversation with your doctor.

Finally, how long do you want to live? I'd like to know what you're thinking, so write or E-mail me with your opinion at the addresses listed at the beginning of this book. ◆

# CHAPTER TWELVE

# Male Trouble:

## IN OTHER WORDS, THE PROSTATE

*"Every patient needs mouth-to-mouth resuscitation, for talk is the kiss of life."*

—Anatole Broyard

Author and prostate patient Anatole Broyard once said that his urologist was brilliant, but he didn't talk very much. "His brilliance has no voice, at least not when he's with me," Broyard complained. As a result, Broyard wrote in his book *Intoxicated by My Illness* that he longed to talk of the prostate and felt "forced to stop people on the street and talk to them about it." As Freud once pointed out, all cures are, at least partially, talking cures.

Come to think of it, isn't that what this book is about—the chance for us to talk it out, to discuss the ever-challenging, outrageous business of aging? We're working together to help each other maneuver past the rough patches.

It begins for most of us with what doctors describe as "nocturia," getting up at night to void. This march of the melancholy males begins most nights before 2:00 A.M. A second expedition follows around 4:00 in the morning and then a third, fourth, even fifth bathroom sojourn comes during those murky hours before daylight. These are the opening vignettes in the sobering life-drama which describes an older male and his problematic prostate. Put directly, it is all about urinating—frequently yet hesitantly, slowly, and sometimes incompletely. To use the street vernacular, a prostate sufferer gives a "piss poor performance."

Anatomically, a man's prostate gland sits under his bladder and surrounds his urethra, the canal for carrying off urine. In size and shape, it resembles a horse chestnut and is made of glandular tissue and some muscle. Beginning some time after age 45, the prostate goes through an odd "second phase" of growth and can compress or squeeze the urethra, narrowing this vital outflow channel.

When asked by a reader for my views on the prostate, the most diseased organ in the male body, I again turned to Broyard, who wrote, "What a curious organ. What can God have been thinking when he designed it this way?" I'm also partial to the description found in a Rodale Press newsletter: "For most of a man's life, the prostate behaves like a gentleman. But around middle age, it often starts acting up."

This is profound understatement. The following statistics summarize the trouble we males endure with a gland that we'd rather not have.

Cancer of the prostate is the most common malignancy in men, and the second leading cause of cancer deaths (24.4 deaths per 100,000) after lung cancer (74.7 per 100,000).

During 1996, more than 317,000 men in the United States received the news they had prostate cancer and, according to the American Cancer Society, some 42,000 men died that year from their disease.

Researchers suspect there may be two species of prostate cancer—an aggressive, fast-growing variety and an "indolent," or slow-growing, tumor.

This malignancy kills 100 men every day and demographers predict that one of every five men will develop cancer of the prostate. It is also estimated that by age 50, four out of ten men will have some cancerous cells in their prostate. By age 60, that percentage jumps to 50 percent, or one of every two men.

Does all this signify that prostate cancer is epidemic in the United States today? Perhaps, but keep in mind that men are living longer, so tumors have more time to develop. And some people believe that the increase of incidence reflects an improved ability to find prostate tumors through ultrasound and blood tests which screen for a prostate-specific antigen (PSA).

For our purposes, let's assume a cautionary approach based on the wisdom of the late Dr. Willet Whitmore, a giant in his field and once the chief of urology at New York's Memorial Sloan-Kettering Hospital. "Growing old is invariably fatal," he explained. "Prostate cancer is only sometimes so."

While I was editor of *50 Plus* magazine, Dr. Keith B. Taylor, then a professor of medicine at Stanford University, wrote an article for me on the prostate. He stated "Presumably, as autopsy studies have shown, every male would eventually develop prostate cancer if he lived long enough, but the majority die of other causes before symptoms appear."

I prefer to emphasize that most prostate cancers are microscopic and, according to a 1993 *Consumer Reports* study, grow too slowly ever to pose a threat. Even if prostate cancer is diagnosed, it's difficult to know whether treating the cancer will improve a man's life expectancy and *quality of life*. Or as Marilyn Chase wrote in the *Wall Street Journal:* "Prostate cancer is that paradox of modern medicine: a disease that doctors have learned to diagnose long before they have reached consensus about how to treat it."

Based on this logic, the operative term here becomes "watchful waiting." This means that you and your doctor join in an accord to do next to nothing for the time being. The watchful part also means you appear regularly for checkups, including blood work and the dreaded DRE (digital rectal exam). This is a conservative approach, a regimen which spares you from major surgery and the risk of unwelcome post-operative results, notably impotence and/or urinary incontinence.

Dr. William Fair of Memorial Sloan-Kettering Cancer Center tells a story about the negative effects of those dreaded "I" words—incontinence and impotence—that follow many surgeries. "When I ask a man after treatment 'How is sex now?' he'll often say fine. Then I look at his wife and she's shaking her head no."

Not every man who learns he has (or probably has) cancer will agree to do nothing. General H. Norman Schwartzkopf, the ebullient hero of the Gulf War, was told in 1994, when he was only 59, that he was sick with cancer of the prostate. The good news was the cancer had not spread. He decided at once to have surgery, a radical prostatectomy, declaring he was not someone "who knows I have a cancer growing inside me and can live with the knowledge."

In the July 1997 issue of the *Journal of the American Medical Association,* researchers at the University of Miami reported on their study of 3,600 men who had their prostates surgically removed between 1983–87. The study showed those with non-aggressive tumors did well. In fact, only 5 percent of these men died of prostate cancer within ten years. Many others, however, died of other causes. Those with aggressive tumors that had spread beyond the prostate did poorly. Up to 40 percent of these men died from their disease during the same ten-year span.

In addition to the surgical removal of the gland, there are other treatments for prostate cancer, each with its proponents and critics. These treatments include hormonal therapy; a therapy that uses high-energy radiation to kill cancer cells; a process called brachytherapy, during which radioactive seeds are implanted throughout the prostate; and cryosurgery, a new technique that kills cancer cells by freezing the prostate gland.

Which is the preferred treatment, the one with the best score card? Medical science cannot yet tell because these therapies have never been compared in clinical trials. Dr. Michael K. Brawer, chief of urology at the VA Medical Center in Seattle, explains, "It is impossible to say that one of them is more effective than the others. That means [all] treatment must be tailored to the individual."

If you are faced with a critical decision about your prostate, you'll need to have a number of long talks with your doctor and follow up with your own research, reading, and study. If you're married, you must include your partner in your ultimate decision and it's of paramount importance that your doctor knows your goal, your preferences, and your rationale. It hardly needs saying that what you are dealing with is a matter, quite possibly, of life and death.

Because I am an optimist, and because I cannot resist a good yarn, I've chosen to round out this chapter with the story of Tom Alexander, a writer, a thinker, and a most convincing advocate for watchful waiting.

"I get a lot of calls and letters from people wondering, I suspect, whether I'm dead yet," he wrote in *Fortune* magazine almost three years after he first announced that, at age 62, he had a relatively small prostate tumor. Tom explained in his original *Fortune* article, "One Man's Tough Choices on Prostate Cancer," that he had elected *not* to have the surgery or radiation which had been recommended by his doctor. Instead, he voted for watchful waiting and "was joining an enormous cohort of scared and bewildered men."

A former staff writer for *Fortune*, Alexander built his own retirement home up in the Smoky Mountains of western North

Carolina out of logs he cut and hewed. He is not the average guy, nor the average prostate sufferer, and makes the point forcefully when he writes, "For the moment, I have no symptoms and I find living with prostate cancer gets easier all the time. The actual mortality and even the relative risk are, after all, not very different from auto fatalities, but who hesitates to jump into a car?"

Alexander had discovered, from his reading and interviewing, that ". . .there was dispute over whether any of the known treatments was likely to prolong my life or, if it did, whether the prospective few weeks or months that might be added to the end of my life would outweigh the potential damage to life's quality, starting now."

This unorthodox patient—is he a prostate pioneer?—confesses he continues to hope for ten or fifteen years "untroubled by the negative effects of either cancer or its treatments, during which time maybe some of the promising current research on genes and immunity may finally pay off with real answers to this weird disease of ours."

"Did you tick off the medical establishment with your attitude?" I asked Alexander in a telephone interview.

"Oh, I don't think so," he answered, and we both had a laugh at the prospect. "I think some of them have changed their minds. They're even handing out copies of my articles to patients."

There are two other facts which stand out from Alexander's stories and bear repeating. The United States is almost alone in its "enthusiasm for aggressive treatment [of prostate cancer], despite conflicting evidence as to whether it does much good." And the decision to have major surgery (a prostatectomy) comes from "older patients, and often at their insistence."

In a gesture that can only be viewed as remarkably generous, Tom Alexander gives out his phone number—(704) 926-9572—so that other men, most of whom are scared and bewildered have some place to go with their negative emotions, some way to connect with someone who will truly listen and discuss, to the best of his considerable abilities.

Men are reluctant to talk about a disease that goes to the heart of their sexuality until it strikes them—and then they have no choice. To be able to hold up his end of the bargain and stay knowledgeable and current, Tom Alexander now begins many mornings on the Internet "talking" with and learning from other prostate guys.

That's the way it is and should be with us outrageous types. We should be reaching out to help one another because every man will have problems with his prostate at some time in his life. When this trouble comes, the man who is alone will have a terrible time managing his fears and reaching difficult decisions as to treatment. Whether he knows it or not, this man needs the help of other men.

Time and again as I researched this chapter, I heard that the prostate is not a matter of one problem leading to one solution. It is a rough patch calling for knowledge, camaraderie, and hope.

# The "Benign" Prostate

The most common or prevalent prostate problem is BPH, benign prostatic hyperplasia, which is characterized by non-cancerous and progressive enlargement of the prostate. More than half of all men in their 60s, and as many as 90 percent in their 70s and 80s, experience symptoms of BPH, including:

1. a weak or interrupted urinary stream

2. a feeling that you cannot empty your bladder completely

3. a feeling of delay or hesitation when you start to urinate

4. a need to urinate often, especially at night

5. a feeling that you must urinate right away.

Ready for the good news? BPH is considered a treatable condition and there are now a battery of medications that can bring a patient relief. These drugs block muscle contractions and relax the structures around the lower part of the bladder and urethra. There also are drugs to shrink the prostate.

In addition, there are common sense measures that could help the situation. For example:

Stay away from liquids after the dinner hour but be sure not to cut down on your total liquid intake. Fluids are important for keeping your system running properly.

As you must know, alcohol and caffeine are diuretics that promote the flow of urine. Avoid them as much as you can. Find substitute drinks. I'm partial to sports drinks, such as Gatorade.

If your doctor has prescribed diuretics for high blood pressure or a heart condition, speak with him or her about the time of day you take your medication. Or you might change to another type of diuretic to help with your prostate trouble. ◆

# To Test or Not to Test?

You cannot write about the prostate without using the word "controversial." Nowhere is that more true than in addressing the blood test known as the prostate-specific antigen or PSA exam. There are two sharply divided camps on the matter. One group argues the PSA is the best weapon in the early warning detection camp. The other side calls the PSA a decidedly imperfect test, an exam riddled with false negatives and false positives. In other words, you can record a low (good) PSA and still have cancer. Or you can have a high (bad) PSA with no cancer.

For example, an enlarged prostate (benign prostatic hyperplasia) or a urinary tract infection can cause PSA levels to rise. According to *Consumer Reports,* up to two-thirds of positive tests are false and, in fact, there's no cancer present. The group adds, "There's no doubt the PSA test can raise nearly as many questions as it answers."

While specialists (urologists) favor the test, internists and other family practice doctors are among those who worry routine PSA screening is certain to frighten large numbers of men for no purpose. They point out that men in their 70s are unlikely to develop a prostate cancer that will cause their death, so for them the PSA makes no sense. Most prostate cancers are slow-growing and only one in every 380 men diagnosed with prostate cancer dies of it. However, you should note that the rate of prostate cancer among African-Americans is the highest in the world, and so far, no one knows why this is true. Some doctors recommend that African-American men begin their prostate testing at age 40.

The PSA test is a radioimmunoassay that measures the concentration of a type of protein present only in the human prostate. Minute amounts of PSA are normally found in the circulatory system. This amount rises when prostate cancer is present and the concentration is related to the size and activity of the abnormal growth.

A man's PSA count is measured in billionths of a gram (nanograms) per millimeter of blood. Until very recently, a PSA level over 4.0 raised suspicions of malignancy. But new studies have shown that somewhat higher levels in older men need not cause alarm. Finally, you should know that even health organizations differ on the importance of the PSA exam and its individual findings. The American Cancer Society recommends screening in men 50 and older while the American

BE AN OUTRAGEOUS OLDER MAN

College of Physicians and the National Cancer Institute do not. An NCI spokesperson says, however, that the question is under study. ◆

# Want Help?

These are groups you may want to contact for more information or literature on the prostate.

**US TOO (800) 808-7866**

(This is a self-help group where patients meet to exchange information and share experiences.)

**The American Cancer Society (800) ACS-2345**

**American Prostate Society (800) 308-1106**

**The National Cancer Institute (800) 4-Cancer**

The following are books that discuss the myriad problems of the prostate.

*The Prostate: A Guide for Men and the Women Who Love Them,* Patrick Walsh, M.D., and Janet Worthington (Johns Hopkins; $15.95)

*Prostate and Cancer,* Sheldon Marks, M.D. (Fisher Books; $14.95)

You may want to ask your public librarian about these books.◆

# CHAPTER THIRTEEN

# Exercise

## IS YOUR TICKET TO THE LONGER LIFE WORTH LIVING

*"Exercise should be taken with an equal amount of play. It should not be like the medicine we down. . . It should be a reward, a time set apart to enjoy, alone or with others."*

—George Sheehan, M.D., writing in *Personal Best*

W hen my friend Ed Kiester, an inveterate downhill skier at the age of 65-plus years, broke his right hand at the base of the thumb, he dismissed this calamity as a freak accident. Californians have a way of believing they're healthier—and less vulnerable—than other Americans. However, when his cast came off six weeks later, Kiester looked down at his shrunken forearm and wrist and said, "It's as though this part of my body is 90 years old."

Ed's arm suffered from the same condition your body will if you don't exercise regularly. The condition is called disuse.

The lesson in this chapter is simply this—if you want to ensure a miserable old age, don't exercise.

Physiologists and other medical scientists refer to disuse of the body as a hypokinetic disease, an ailment caused by lack of movement. The results of disuse—of being sedentary, of getting little or no movement—are devastating. The point is that many of the so-called "effects of aging" are, in fact, the end products of disuse. Author John Jerome, a friend and perhaps the finest writer on exercise in the United States, has said, "In the most carefully designed scientific test, it is virtually impossible to discriminate between the effects of aging and the effects of inactivity."

Simply stated, if exercise could be bottled or fabricated into a pill, it would be the most widely prescribed medication in the world. That is the opinion of Dr. Bob Butler and others who have suggested that one day soon it may be *prima facie* malpractice for a doctor *not* to prescribe exercise for the senior patient, whatever his or her ailment.

In Boston, at the Human Nutrition Center on Aging, researchers have proved that sedentary seniors, 60- and 70-year-old men, profit from strength training. Describing this work in *Biomakers: The 10 Determinants of Aging You Can Control,* authors William Evans, Ph.D., and Dr. Irwin H. Rosenberg write that "No group in our population can benefit more from exercise than senior citizens, as startling a statement as that may seem at first blush. Indeed, the muscles of elderly people are just as responsive to weight lifting as those of younger people."

Later in their book, the authors explain that muscle is responsible for the vitality "of your whole physiological apparatus." After stating that muscle mass and strength become the primary markers of biological aging, Evans and Rosenberg write, "Building muscle mass in the elderly is the key to their rejuvenation [and] exercise is the key to a healthy and rewarding old age."

Now, don't let all the talk of muscles and strength put you off or intimidate you. All along the exercise front there is good news for you. Exercise isn't what it used to be. You can forget the one-armed pushups, running marathons, or rolling about the turf in T-shirts and shorts to prove you're still macho. "No pain, no gain" has gone the way of dime beer and trolley cars. What we're talking about here is movement, of getting outdoors and walking, biking, swimming, gardening (weeding is wonderful for the waistline), and dancing. Or playing softball, tennis, even golf, and, in the meantime, looking better, feeling stronger, and living healthier.

This is the kind of stuff you did as a kid during recess and after school until darkness chased you indoors. We're talking about play, active play, and you can start this very minute. Walk toward the nearest mirror and, staring inward, repeat your new mantra:

"I'll do it. . . I'll begin today. . . and I'll keep at it three, four times a week."

Now, if you promise not to laugh, I'll confess a personal secret. I've liked to jump rope for years and still go at it on a regular basis. I own a prize-fighter's leather rope with weighted handles which adds an upper body workout while I'm doing my heart a great big favor, skipping from one foot the other.

For me, rope skipping began when, as a rotund teenager (face it, Lindeman: you were fat!), I was sent home from a failed tennis lesson with explicit instructions to learn to jump rope before attempting tennis. My problem then was a total lack of quickness and agility. Overtaking a tennis ball was beyond me.

In a small, second-story prize-fighters' gym in Hackensack, NJ,

I was taught to challenge my awkward body, to skip rope correctly, to throw a punch from the shoulder, and to hit a speed bag so that it would give off that telltale rat-a-tat-tat rhythm. For me, this boy wanting to be man, it was all play, so I never noticed the boring, repetitious, tedious qualities associated with repetitive exercise.

Am I suddenly advocating that you drop your year-old plans to put up wallpaper in the downstairs bathroom, or cancel your Caribbean cruise in order to take rope-skipping lessons? Negative. What I am suggesting is that you must battle, fiercely and with all your determination, against the devastating American tendency toward hypokinesis: too little movement. Find an activity or exercise that turns you on, one that in your mind is play, and make a commitment to it.

"The ability to influence another person's root behavior is one of the most challenging issues of humanity," writes Dr. Walter M. Bortz II, a veritable exercise fanatic as well as eminent clinician and Stanford University Medical School faculty member. "Perversely, we seem to adopt destructive modes much more easily than constructive ones. . . I believe ten Nobel prizes should await that person who can write the guidelines for how we can help the deteriorating individual take care of himself."

In *We Live Too Short and Die Too Long*, Bortz addresses the basic elements of health: exercise, diet, and sleep, and adds, "Of the three, adequate exercise has primacy." Following this, he does his best to convince us beyond all doubt that exercise wards off disease and extends life.

This medical author and committed runner cites research studies to support his conclusion that "inactivity is lethal [and] fitness becomes more important to survival the older we become. . . as we age, physical conditioning becomes increasingly predictive of survival."

The unarguable conclusion is that health payoffs from physical activity are compelling and continuous. I shall cite two research examples.

A study of London bus conductors is a favorite among exercise supporters. Investigators found that the conductors who walked up and down stairs while working on the city's notable double-decker buses were half as likely to suffer heart attacks as the sedentary drivers who sat all day.

Perhaps the most convincing study about the positive effects of exercise on aging was carried out by Dr. Ralph Paffenbarger. He followed 17,000 Harvard University graduates over the course of forty years. Those who expended 2,000 calories a week in physical activities reduced their death rates from all causes by a remarkable 28 percent. Two thousand calories of exercise a week is roughly equivalent to an hour's brisk walk every day. As a result of their regular exercise, these men lived an average of 2.15 years longer than their less active classmates.

Still need convincing? Well, the American Heart Association now lists the absence of regular exercise as a risk factor, citing it as a public enemy right up there with smoking, obesity, high blood pressure, stress, diabetes, and a family history of heart disease.

In an article written for the heart association, Howard L. Lewis states that a good argument can be made that physical inactivity is the number one health problem facing people in the United States. According to heart specialists, only 10 to 20 percent of adults "are appropriately active, while 30 percent get no exercise at all." Shame on this nation of couch potatoes.

After absorbing this information for a day or two, I sat down and wrote this lead for a column entitled "Do Yourself a Big Favor—Start Exercising."

"We wait impatiently for a cure for cancer. We hope we shall soon tame the disease-beast that is Alzheimer's. Then there is heart disease, the number one killer of both men and women. In a calendar year, more than one million Americans will die as a result of heart and blood vessel disease. Can you imagine the headlines, the accolades and tributes if tomorrow the President of the United States could announce that there was a cure for heart disease? The Nobel prize committee would be summoned into extraordinary session."

Well, the fact is, we have "discovered" something almost as good. We have found a way to pretty much prevent heart disease, a method to hold this tiger of a disease at bay. No, it's not a pill or vaccine or some wonder drug. Moreover, no pharmaceutical manufacturer controls it. On the contrary, it's within your power to immediately take up the cure. Sure, we can self-medicate to our heart's content. The preventive medicine is simply e-x-e-r-c-i-s-e!

I'll step down from my bully pulpit now, closing with this twice-told story. As he approached his half-century anniversary some years ago, John Jerome determined to become an athlete again. He began serious training in order to equal, or better, his high school times as a competitive swimmer. Jerome describes his triumph in understatement in his book *Staying With It*.

"A little over two years after I started training and about six months short of my 50th birthday, I swam a 100-yard freestyle race in 0:55.99. This was two full seconds faster than my best time for the same race when I was 18. It would be hard to over-state the significance of that comparison to me."

You either push against the physical envelope—your body— or, sadly, you lose the use of it to the aging process. Jerome writes that "One of aging's most powerful effects seems to be the shrinking, dwindling, loss of range of motion, stiffness, mal-function of joints, reduced stature, and other related connective-tissue ailments for which the ONLY antidote I've been able to find is movement—exercise and stretching."

Jerome isn't the first to make these observations and pro-nouncements. Plato once declared, "The body is the source of energy." Indeed, we are our bodies and our bodies are us.

If you want to be an outrageous older man, then you've got to use your body.

# Getting Started

How does the average Joe Blow, who is more couch potato than all-American athlete, get started on an exercise regimen? Here are some points that make good sense and, given a fair trial, should work to get you off your duff and into the active mode:

**Rule one:** Make your workouts enjoyable. Find a sport or activity that's right for you, and be faithful to it. Swimming is my favorite sport—and my relaxation. I'm convinced water is therapeutic. I also enjoy talking with the other swimmers I meet. In this way, my workout provides good exercise and social activity.

If companionship is important to you, join an exercise class. You can also enlist a buddy to work out with you and help in the motivation department. Or you could use a personal trainer.

**Rule two:** Set realistic goals. Remember, this is meant to be your pattern for a lifetime so it must be both comfortable and practical. For the first week, be content with a simple 20-minute workout or, if you'd rather, a half-mile walk. Next week: one mile. After a month, go for two miles every second day.

To build on your comfort quotient, buy yourself a snazzy workout suit and a log or diary. Over time, you'll want to review your exercise activity—and do some gloating about your progress.

On days when you don't walk, swim, or otherwise exercise, hit the weights. As we age, we lose muscle mass and strength training can help prevent this. Besides, variety in your workouts will help keep you from going stale and dreading your gym-time.

**Rule three:** Have a backup plan. If you've scheduled a two-mile walk and it rains (or snows), head for the gym and the treadmill. Every exercise buff says the same thing, "I get bored. That's when I switch to biking, or swimming." To which I add, "Jumping rope takes so little time and space, requires next to no equipment, and is a serious cardiovascular workout." When you're done, after 10 or 15 minutes of intermittent skipping, you can say, "That was outrageous!"

**Last rule:** Please don't get intimidated by the super fit, those hard bodies looking at themselves in the mirrors. There are very few world-class athletes, and your goal is not to make an Olympic squad. The name of your game is improved cardiovascular and musculoskeletal health.

Look better. Feel better. Sleep better. Work better. All of these benefits await you when you make the decision to believe sincerely that "We become what we do!" ◆

# A Personal Story

With all my might, I was struggling, straining on one of those torturous weight machines, seeking to pull 70 pounds towards me with two very tired arms, both 69 years old. I tried to remember—was this the sixth or seventh repetition? Suddenly, I let out an involuntary scream, "No way would I work this hard alone!" Standing over me, seemingly oblivious to my pain in pursuit of gain, was my trainer, Steve Bryant, age 28 and determined. In his pocket, he carries business cards that read "Body Construction."

I willingly confess to this humbling moment to make a point. All around me are examples of senior men behaving outrageously. In fairness, how could I be their chronicler, their cheerleader and spokes-guy if I didn't join their burgeoning movement in some way? Therefore, I signed up in a weight lifting gym and Bryant, this veritable kid, became my mentor. He is also my drill sergeant, my conscience, and when I elect to tease him, "the Warden."

Twice a week, for an hour at a time, I willingly submit to his urging and encouragements. We move expeditiously from machine to machine, doing leg curls, leg extensions, calf raises, sit-squats (your back is pressed against an oversized rubber ball and you slowly go up and down), and a cruel assortment of five or six arm exercises. When it's over, I am finished, spent. Later, following a shower and sometimes a nap, I feel renewed, refreshed—and confident.

Do I also have more energy? Decidedly so. Am I exemplary or unusual in this regard? Not in the least. Young Bryant wants me to be stronger. I'm content to pursue continued good health, including the ability to perform any and all activities that I choose. Strength training is my ticket to this destination. What do you say? Want to give it a try? ◆

# CHAPTER FOURTEEN

# How Does

## YOUR GARDEN GROW?

*"Anyone who keeps the ability
to see beauty never grows old."*

—Franz Kafka

Veteran Atlanta journalist Lee May, who is nothing if not outrageous, sees the world through a very different prism. His profession as well as his passion is gardening. He believes that, "No matter what the career or who the person is, gardening is an incredibly seductive destination." We first met over lunch to swap lies and to talk of writers and their books. Before long, May was proselytizing, explaining that gardening could even be considered a gift for grandchildren.

"What better way to teach them the lessons of success and failure?" he asked. "Along with a respect for nature, self-sufficiency, even gentleness. They'll also grow to understand the value and beauty of a space free of discarded candy bags and soda cans," he continued. "Once a child tends a garden, well, trashing the ground becomes difficult."

Every spring, as warm weather travels from south to north, millions of men, women, and children of all ages put loving hands into dirt, mulch, compost, fertilizers, weeds, grass, plants, and, on occasion, poison ivy. The National Gardening Association says that more than half the households in the United States boast at least one gardener, with the total exceeding 76 million. America's green thumb brigades also spend an estimated $22.5 billion on seeds, equipment, flowers, and vegetables during a twelve-month period.

Moreover, nearly every gardener feels good about all that digging, planting, pruning, and cultivating. Older adults with whom I've talked accept that gardening is an avocation, relaxation, exercise, ritual, and perhaps even a necessity, because it is a balm for the soul. I recall hearing "Gardening, like opera, hits us in the second half of life." As the editor of *50 Plus* magazine, I once published a story called "Tough Guys Grow Petunias" in which we reported that 700 prisons and clinics used gardening as part of the rehabilitation process. "Planting a row of beans or pulling weeds does a wonderful job of making us feel at peace with ourselves and our surroundings," author Stephen Brewer explained.

Lee May understands all this and more. "I have come to know that a garden is many things beyond a place to grow flowers or foods," he states. "It is sanctuary, exercise room, and a place for rehabilitation. One more thing—it's almost impossible to find a gardener who is a bad person, even an ornamental gardener."

The man with these confident opinions regularly writes about gardens and those who tend them. He became a weekly columnist at the *Atlanta Journal-Constitution* after serving the *Los Angeles Times* for twelve years as a Washington correspondent and then Atlanta bureau chief. Thus, May has gone from covering foul deeds, including corruption, murder, riots, and other random violence—the hairy-chested stuff from which journalism prizes and rewards flow—to what traditionally has been considered the women's corner of the newspaper. He couldn't be happier or more content.

He also set down many of his cogent views on gardening and life in a memoir he called *In My Father's Garden.* May writes in this poignant work of taking white friends home to his mother's for chitlins and other delicacies sometimes referred to as "soul food." As a result of the harmony that pervaded these get-togethers, Lee May was able to see beyond the numerous episodes of racism that marked his young life. He concluded, "Sharing and enjoying a meal with somebody of another color makes you believe that racial peace is possible."

Throughout his 216-page book, which recounts how he and his birth father reunited without anger or recrimination after 39 years, May keeps coming back to his genuine familial love for gardening. It has become his metaphor, his soul connection. These are two of my favorite Lee observations.

"A good garden comes as much from the soul as it does from the pocketbook."

"I have seen the power of the idea of gardening reflected in children's eyes, and I love it; it shines in such delightful contrast to the dead eyes that stare hollowly from so many young heads."

After I read May's book and had been a witness to his fervor, I was determined to become a suburban amateur gardener. Now, two years later, I tend two acres in Stone Mountain, GA, where azaleas, dogwoods, boxwoods, daylilies, roses, rhododendrons, marigolds, hydrangeas, crepe myrtles, camellias, and perhaps a hundred pines and hardwood trees are my responsibility. Two fine neighbors, both retired gentlemen, help me as I stumble, question, transplant, and begin anew each season. Clyde Baxter, Alabama-born, and Harry Primm, originally from Tennessee, are both patient and kind with this "new Georgian," a late life convert to the great outdoors.

My vocabulary and my shopping habits have changed—Home Depot and Pike's Nursery are two of my favorite weekend haunts—and a thrill for me these days is not a tall gin and tonic nor a smooth transition in a column, but a yellow or pink rose in first flower. I've read that when men are no longer in the business of procreating human beings, they long for a way to leave their mark on society. To turn a patch of ground into a veritable riot of pastel azalea blooms framed by the soft, white flowers of dogwoods, well, that is "high cotton" as we say down here in the South.

In 1845, Ezra Weston of the Massachusetts Horticultural Society wrote, "He who cultivates a garden, and brings to perfection flowers and fruits, cultivates and advances at the same time his own nature."

I believe that. And I'm hard at it, working today and tomorrow to advance my own nature, my essence.

# You Can Have Your Hobby, and Eat It, Too

V egetable gardeners know the thrill of biting into a tomato or cucumber they've grown and experiencing a wonderful home grown taste. This makes gardening the rare sideline where you get to eat your hobby.

Whether your interest lies in vegetable gardening or Japanese gardens, the American Horticultural Society has compiled a list of guides, references, and special interest books which you can obtain free of charge by writing: **AHS Booklist,** PO Box 0105, Mt. Vernon, VA 22121.

You may also want to know that many community colleges sponsor courses for novice gardeners. The American Horticultural Society offers a pamphlet entitled "Educational Institutions Offering Horticultural and Landscape Architecture Programs in the United States and Canada." There is a small charge for the booklet.

Other groups offering information include:

**National Gardening Association,** 180 Flynn Ave., Burlington, VT 05401

**American Community Gardening Association,** PO Box 93147, Milwaukee, WI 53202

**National Council of State Garden Clubs,** Inc., 4401 Magnolia Ave., St. Louis, MO 63110-3492 You can receive information from this organization about gardening clubs in your area.

There is no older men's group devoted to gardening that I know of. Shouldn't there be one? Maybe even an Outrageous Older Gardener's Association. If you have an opinion, or are interested in fostering such an idea, please contact me at the addresses provided at the beginning of this book. ◆

# OUTRAGEOUS
## *Actions*

# CHAPTER FIFTEEN

# Change

## IS GOOD

*"The absurd man*
*is he who never changes."*

—Auguste Barthélémy

M y adult children are of one opinion on the matter—it's the most outrageous thing I've ever done.

They refer to it as The Move, an action which led me to become the owner of a house, a yard that won't quit, and a beloved dog. Here's the clincher—all of this is well south of the Mason-Dixon line. Nowadays my kids ask, "When are you getting a pickup, Dad?"

For fifteen years, I had lived high above the Hudson River on the New Jersey shore. My address was immediately opposite the 79th Street boat basin in New York City, or more specifically, Manhattan. Toward evening, the lights began blinking on and, once darkness fell, the entire island was lit from the George Washington Bridge south to Battery Park. That dramatic vista became my private view, or so it seemed. It is a sight no thinking man will ever forget, and it certainly is a good reason to live in a high rise condominium in Guttenberg, NJ.

F. Scott Fitzgerald wrote of the "enchanted metropolitan twilight," when he knew "a haunting loneliness sometimes, and felt it in others." Author Willie Morris, a proud southerner from Yazoo City, MS, celebrated the "impervious play of dusk and dark on its concrete and glass. . . New York City in those very first moments was all radiance and adumbra for me, all swirling lights and blending shadow."

I was born in New York City, carved out a modest career as a newsman, then a magazine writer, and much later, a magazine editor. With all its faults, and I knew them well, New York was my hometown. It was the place where I learned to cover fires, murders, stupid politicians (I don't mean to be redundant), and those unforgettable stories about genuine people rising above the chaos to help another soul. It was where I was introduced to Ernest Hemingway at Toots Shor's old tavern, where I reported about the Brooklyn Dodgers in their only World Series triumph, and where I made my first reaffirming male friendships, some that last to this day.

It was also the hometown of my mother and father, and I grew up listening to their tales of the magical New York of the 1920s. Even today, I can walk the residential streets and hear the siren voice of Martha Quitzau Lindeman telling me about Carl Schurz Park, and innocent girlhood days and nights in the Yorkville section of town where the Germans and Scandinavians settled.

I grew fond of telling people that I lived in the most cerebral city in the world. You could strike up a conversation in an elevator or office cubicle that might amount to chitchat or, conceivably, continue as an intellectual dialogue over a lifetime.

New York is also one of the most expensive cities to live in— and it can be violent and cruel beyond comprehension. It's difficult avoiding both of these realities. Jan Still had moved from

Atlanta to marry me, and thirteen years later she decided it was the husband's turn to pack up and relocate.

In fairness, we had both burned out, professionally speaking, and Jan needed to be closer to her folks. Her late father, whom she loved and loved to please, had recurring problems with a diseased heart valve. This meant we were trying to be long-distance caregivers—and it wasn't working.

As an inveterate New Yorker, I didn't drive. More to the point, I had let my license lapse in the 1970s. So Jan rented the haul-it-yourself truck, and like a pair of Okies leaving the dust bowl of the 1930s, we headed south. In Virginia, we ran smack up against a howling winter storm. Welcome to the South, Yankees!

A day later, I knew we were in Dixie when I spotted my first downhome bumper sticker—Buckle Up With Jesus. At first we lived in a small apartment in Doraville, GA, a place renowned for nothing but its proximity to Atlanta. Then, almost two years later, we took possession of a rambling, old wood and stone house. This home lies almost in the shadow of a storied carving honoring heroes of the Confederacy. This majestic relief, carved into the side of Stone Mountain, commands a view of a beautiful state park four miles from our front door.

Almost immediately, I bought a lawn mower, two types of rakes, hedge clippers, and all the assorted paraphernalia needed to once again become a keeper of suburban lawns. It took me no time at all to fall back in love with that lifestyle. Now at the close of a hot summer's day, I can float in our backyard pool, stare up at the tall pines, oaks, maples, dogwoods, and poplar trees and ask myself, "Is this good, or what?"

But am I a southerner? Not entirely. I tell friends I'm going to a dermatologist because my red neck isn't taking, and I still haven't seen the Georgia Bulldogs bump heads with another Southeast Conference rival. Nonetheless, I am proud to report that I belong to the Georgia Gerontology Society and am the volunteer editor of its newsletter. And I enjoy the work of our fine crop of local writers, people such as Paul Hemphill (*Leaving Birmingham*) and master storyteller Terry Kay (*To Dance with the White Dog*).

The fact is, I've lived in New York, New Jersey, Vermont (as a collegian), Massachusetts (as a soldier), Texas, Florida, Illinois, and Japan. I believe it is possible, even probable, that you will be content wherever you live if you are happy with your work and have your health. What I'm talking about here is the ability to adapt, to change, to remain open to new experiences, even adventures. I am convinced that this quality is central to successful aging.

In my files, I keep the following quote from Dr. Kenneth R. Pelletier, a California psychiatrist and student of aging. "Psychological adjustments through life are more important than genetics and other biological factors" in determining longevity and general health.

You don't have to seek out change or voluntarily drive 900 miles into another culture and climate to learn how to adapt. Just know that you're not about to get through this life without having some dynamic forced upon you. Change may be only around the corner, waiting to be thrust upon you because of widowhood, divorce, retirement, being fired, financial change, sickness, random crime, or the comings and goings of your adult children.

Behavioral psychologist and author B. F. Skinner once wrote, "If you were planning to spend the rest of your life in another country, you would learn as much about it as possible. You would read books. . . You would talk with people who had lived there. You might even learn a bit of its language. Old age is rather like another country. You will enjoy it more if you have prepared yourself before you go."

Skinner might also have added that you would be well advised to prepare yourself for change, for adaptations. In summary, isn't that what aging is all about—the ability to cope? Yes, to cope with change.

# A Love Story—with a Waggly Tail

*"Properly trained, a man can be dog's best friend."*
—Corey Ford

I have fallen head over tea kettle in love again, and in the autumnal years of my life. Since I work at home—and my wife doesn't—my lover and I see each other constantly. The giddy truth is that we're openly, unashamedly affectionate. We simply don't care who sees us.

Here's the biggest surprise—my wife doesn't give a fig. In truth, Jan believed from the outset that the athletic newcomer to our household would prove to be a boon, an elixir or tonic, for us both. She was right. For Nicky, our dark-eyed, floppy-eared, four-legged marvelous mutt is a lover to us both and a compelling reason to roll out of bed each morning.

In New Jersey, we had been cat people. But this was Georgia and we were going to have to change, so we set out to find ourselves a dog. We didn't know whether Nicky was a stray or an abandoned animal when we rescued him from the county animal shelter. He was cautious, even withdrawn, when he entered our home. My wife grew up on a north Georgia farm and remains an incorrigible animal lover. With a tinge of sadness in her voice, she asked, "Do you think he can become a loving pet? I mean, affectionate?"

I had no good answer at the time, yet I like to mimic that question these nights when The Nickster—he answers to a variety of names—is sprawled high up on my wife's chest, his front paws just under her chin, and his adoring brown eyes locked onto her baby blues.

"If he were any more loving than he is," I tell her, "I'd have to sue for divorce."

By day, Nicky is my shadow, the barker-in-chief in our home, and the third leg on the family stool. Truth is, Nicky had used up his days as a county ward when we found him in his stark, flea-ridden cage. He was literally on doggie death row, awaiting a lethal injection, when we chose to bring this two-year-old, unpedigreed canine home. And each of his days is sweeter now because he escaped the animal executioner.

Jan and I are proud to be among the majority of Americans who are animal lovers. In a nation where most people can't agree on where to go for lunch, much less how they feel about assisted death or a balanced budget, 56 percent of the population agrees that we love our pets. My wife and I derive enormous comfort from loving our dog who, we're convinced, was put on earth to make us laugh and feel good about our lives.

Literature and science both tell us we're well advised to follow our hearts in this matter of pets. Poet Walt Whitman wrote, "I think I could turn and live with animals, they are so placid and self-contained." T.S. Eliot observed, "Animals are such agreeable friends—they ask no questions, they pass no criticisms." And writer George Howe Colt explained to the readers of *Life* magazine that "Amid all the forms of life that surround us, not one, excepting the dog, has made an alliance with us."

Through my reading and research, I've learned that dogs are health mates as well as companions. Dog owners have lower blood pressure readings, lower blood cholesterol totals, and, overall, are less susceptible to heart disease than those who are dog-deprived. Further, a University of California medical doctor, Judith Siegel, established that older adults who own pets visit their doctor 16 percent fewer times than those who don't have animal friends.

Dr. Alan Beck, director of the Center for the Interaction of Animals and Society at Purdue University in Indiana, believes that animals provide social validation. In an interview, he said pets afford "loving devotion, constant companionship, an attentive eye, an uncritical ear. They're so attractive to those who have been wounded, and otherwise neglected."

It's all true. The faithful-dog (this can be read as one word) doesn't care if the master or mistress shuffles with arthritis, has one chin too many, perhaps is past due on pesky credit card payments, or frequently forgets where the house keys were last seen. "When we want to play, they chase our tennis balls, catch our Frisbees, even howl along when we sing," wrote George Colt. "When we ruminate on the unfairness of the world, they gaze up at us and agree with whatever we're thinking."

Yes, dogs comfort older dudes. They regularly boost our self-esteem and lure us out of funks or emotional downturns. If you're fighting the blahs or are alone too often, I urge you invite a dog into your household. Then buy a long, strong leash. Give both yourself and your newfound friend the healthful gift of brisk, daily walks—twenty minutes or more at a time. Repeat twice a day. I can almost guarantee you'll feel better about yourself in a week or three.

It is my belief that outrageous older men should have a socially acceptable hobby, an outlet for pent up energy. Mine comes running every time I call "Nicky. Want to go out?" ◆

# CHAPTER SIXTEEN

# Retirement:

## A FAILED EXPERIMENT?

*"One enormous reservoir of unhappiness
could be drained if we expected older people
to work. . . and allowed them to do so. Work
is the natural antidote to unhappiness."*

—Dr. Alex Comfort

The following is a multiple choice question.
My retirement is
a) a slice of heaven.
b) a sentence to purgatory on earth.

Depending upon your experience and circumstances, you are joyously living out your slice of heaven or, conversely, you've been condemned to suffer in earthly purgatory.

Speaking for myself, I don't believe in retirement, not as we know it today. I think it's a ruse, an economic scheme that's been perpetrated upon the nation. I wouldn't be surprised if this failed social experiment, in its present form, didn't last another generation.

Additionally, it has cast us senior adults in a posture where we're seen as geezers, both greedy and inconsequential, as we aggressively pursue our golf, tennis, shuffleboard, bingo, ocean cruises, cocktails, and Early Bird dinner specials. Indeed, too many people believe we're so intent on senior discounts and our Social Security/Medicare entitlements that we have no time or interest for others, particularly the less fortunate.

When I first floated my anti-retirement idea in my newspaper column, the reaction was swift and vitriolic. A letter came from Latrobe, PA, addressed "Dear Stupid Ass." When my correspondent, Andrew J. Smith, stopped spewing and sputtering to put forth his argument, it surely was worth considering. The basis of Smith's argument for a leisurely retirement in his 60s was predicated upon hard facts. He had worked in steel mills for 41 years and before that had done a soldier's tour of duty in World War II, seeing combat throughout Europe. He wrote how he fought against the Germans, the cold, and other miseries during the historic Battle of the Bulge, all for $17 a month. For that heroic effort, he deservedly earned three battle stars.

He explained further that his work life began when he was forced to drop out of the eighth grade to help support his family. At that time, the Smith family numbered six people, four children plus a mother and father, and the nation was in the Depression.

To Andrew Smith, and all the others who flee jobs requiring grinding manual labor at the first opportunity, I hear you talking. No one of sound mind is going to insist that you men *must* work past 60, or 65, punishing your body beyond reason. That, however, is not the entire issue.

For many—indeed most of us—retirement at age 55, 60, 62, or even 75 is not the best idea. Not for our health, not for our emotional well-being, and certainly not for our financial standing, or lack thereof. After all, isn't retirement just another word for unemployment?

Granted, I have a number of friends and acquaintances who are happy beyond description in retirement. When I asked a fine and generous neighbor if he, like me (the columnist/author), was around the house all day and every day, he vigorously shook his head from side to side.

"Oh, no," he protested. "I play golf three, four times a week."

Wonderful. It's just not for me and I contend that when the time comes, the United States will not be able to afford to retire all the baby boomers as they reach the time-honored age of 65. There are 78 million men and women in this age group, and they are the aggressive, accomplished generation that managed to lower the voting age to 18, ended the Vietnam war, launched the feminist movement, and fought in the civil rights movement. In other words, don't mess with them. Still, who's going to pay for their Social Security, Medicare, and Medicaid? Not Generation X.

I find support for my stand on this hot button issue from writers Stephan M. Pollan and Mark Levine. In an article for *Worth* magazine, they stated that retirement, in fact, was unaffordable for *most Americans*. Besides, they point out, baby boomers are not savers. Pollan and Levine contend their research shows that retirement is a difficult transition for 41 percent of Americans and, they argue, the concept of retirement is built upon four false premises.

**False premise No. 1:** Sixty-five is old. Gerontologists say we live in an increasingly age irrelevant society, and you can tell very little about a person by reporting his age. In Los Angeles, there's a rookie cop who's 60. There are outstanding triathletes in their 60s and 70s, brilliant golfers on the Senior Tour, and star entertainers and authors in their 70s and 80s. I've heard demographers speak of "youth creep." What they mean is that you are not as old, in body or mind, as your father or grandfather when they were your present age.

In 1935, when President Franklin Delano Roosevelt set the

retirement age at 65, the average American lived just under 63 years—and about 54 percent of all men age 65 and older were in the work force. Today, following numerous improvements in Social Security, fewer than 17 percent of all age 65-plus men continue to work. My premise is that they either are forced from their jobs by the early retirement culture (see Chapter Five on age discrimination) or are enticed to leave by Social Security and/or pension payouts.

My question then becomes, "Is this good for the individual? Is it good for the nation?" Colin Gillion, an economist with the International Labor Organization (a United Nations–affiliated group), thinks not. He told a United States Senate hearing that early retirement has a decidedly negative impact, explaining there's an obvious loss of revenue coupled with higher pension outlays. He called this a double cost squeeze that is ill-advised for advanced economies. He told the senators that bonuses and higher pensions should be offered to keep the older, more experienced workers at their jobs.

**False premise No. 2:** Leisure is more fulfilling than work. Well, according to authors Pollan and Levine, during the 1990s an estimated 40 percent of retirees reported they were unhappy being out of the work force. One of these disappointed retirees wrote me that "You feel you are nothing once you stop working."

"Work is an integral part of human life," write authors Pollan and Levine, as they explain how one-third of all men in retirement make some effort to take jobs. Many of these jobs are part time because that's all that's available.

In a column he wrote to accompany Pollan and Levine's provocative anti-retirement article, *Worth's* youthful publisher, W. Randall Jones, said "I have very few friends happily retired. There's a hole in their lives, and it's called work. I can't imagine not wanting to contribute something to the world."

**False premise No. 3:** Older workers need to move over and permit the young to get their fair chance. The idea that older men (and women) must be good citizens and retire is hypocritical at best. In the new leaner, meaner economy, corporations show little loyalty to longtime workers. So where do they get off asking some senior worker to "do his duty" and volunteer for premature retirement? These businesses want their higher paid veterans to disappear, for obvious reasons.

**False premise No. 4:** There is a canard about older workers not being able to cut it. Bogus! Study after study shows that senior workers make fewer mistakes, and have fewer accidents, lower absenteeism, and a stronger work ethic than their younger counterparts.

My favorite lines from Pollan and Levine on this emotionally complex situation read, "Work is not a cliff we scale and then get tossed off at age 65. Rather, it's a hill over which we should plot our own course." In other words, we senior Americans should be afforded the right to decide for ourselves, within reason, when and how to bid good-bye to the work place.

Now, in addition to the letter of chastisement from Andrew Smith, my mail bag also reflected a number of readers, both men and women, who agreed with my "pox on retirement" columns. Ray Frazier of Roselle, IL, wrote, "The thought of having nothing to do the rest of my life was frightening." After 38 years of work in the marketing department of a large corporation, Frazier retired, saying he'd grown "sick of forecasts, quotas, endless stacks of printouts, and the daily pressure of trying to reach goals that were always just beyond attainable levels."

So Ray Frazier bolted out the door and soon thereafter came the awakening. "I quickly realized I'd made a terrible mistake," he said. "I missed the activity, the personal relationships, even the challenges." What then did this disenchanted retiree do? "Rather than 'give it time' as my retired pals suggested, I became the manager of a small company one of my friends owns. Bard, the past four years have been the most enjoyable of my life. Yes, I think it can be good to retire, but only as a *first step* toward starting over."

At *50 Plus* magazine, we called this type of story a "second career" piece. They were a staple for the magazine and always fun to do. The staff grew to enjoy them, perhaps because they spoke to us all. The message in all these stories is, "it's not over yet, not if you will it otherwise."

Radio reporter Connie Goldman made a second (or third) career of traveling the country with a tape recorder and an inquiring mind, interviewing older adults who were, in her words, "late bloomers." She put together a book chock-full of these successful start over people, and did many a segment on National Public Radio featuring her mature bloomers. I particularly like her definition. "By late bloomer, we simply mean anyone who defies the notion that his or her best years are over," she said, "someone who responds to the later stage of life not as a crisis but as a quest."

Late bloomers, I should add, don't retire, not from the workplace and surely not from life.

Speaking personally, I shall continue to put words down on paper for as long as humanly possible. I also intend to see to the lawn, the grounds, and gardens. I shall keep up with my swimming, weightlifting, and other exercises, as well as my expanding, far-flung family. This is the only way I know how to put one day behind another, and to be content.

If you disagree, I want to hear your views. Let's open up this debate on retirement in America. Write me at the addresses at the beginning of the book on how best to balance leisure and work over a long lifetime.

# Read It Here:
## The Key to Successful Retirement

There is an industry devoted to telling you how to retire and discover a diverse, fun-filled life after work. Magazines, books, newsletters, seminars, and videos beckon, for a price. Yet, each of us must walk his or her own way, and it is truly a voyage of self-discovery.

What follows is an essay from a friend who successfully completed that voyage. He is Edward E. Rosenbaum, medical doctor, husband, father, grandfather, author, and recovered cancer patient. He lives in Portland, OR.

*I've decided to answer your nagging questions: When to retire? and how to retire? Understand that I was 33 years old when finally I started my medical practice. I already had five years of residency and five years in the Army during World War II. Of course, I had next to no money. I determined to make it big, though. I wanted to retire at 45 and sail around the world.*

*Well, at 45 I had four sons and a mortgage. It was all I could do to meet the mortgage. At 55, my house was paid up, and my sons were on their way to being educated. I thought, now I can really save some money—money with which to retire at age 65.*

*At 65, I had enough money to live modestly, but why retire when I was in good health? My old idea of sailing around the world wasn't important, at least not now. Besides, if I worked three more years, I figured I could save enough to live in high style. When I turned 68, I said, "Hey, being a doctor is fun!" In addition, I've now got enough money to retire and not worry. I didn't have to work another day.*

*A funny thing happened next. Once I realized I didn't need to work, my practice seemed to become stress free. I told my wife it was more like a hobby. I was enjoying it more than ever. Why quit?*

*At 70, I felt as though I was on top of the world. I had a busy practice with an adequate income. I could afford to be choosy about my working hours. In a burst of euphoria, I signed an office lease for five more years. One month later, a throat specialist told me that, regrettably, I had cancer of the vocal chords. I was forced to look hard at my reality: 1) that trip around the world suddenly was an impossible dream; 2) the money I had so assiduously saved for retirement was useless to me. I doubted I would live to enjoy it.*

*The next year was given over to receiving X-ray treatments for my cancer. I also took daily walks through the woods above my house, and otherwise learned to relax. To this intense, ever-busy physician, relaxation was a skill that needed to be acquired. But as my strength slowly returned,*

*I recognized that my cancer was in remission. This fact encouraged me to write a book about my experiences as a patient.*

*After a year of writing and rewriting, the manuscript was roundly rejected. I started over again. It took me another year and four complete rewrites until the book was pronounced "fit to publish" by Random House. I titled it* A Taste of My Own Medicine *and you'll recall, Bard, you published an excerpt in* 50 Plus *magazine. We both were surprised—and thrilled—when my first book became a big seller.*

*A short time thereafter I took a phone call telling me that Walt Disney Pictures had bid for the movie rights. Since then my quiet, low-keyed world in retirement (forced retirement, that is) has changed. I have dined with scriptwriters and producers to learn that William Hurt, an accomplished actor, would fill my role in the movie,* The Doctor. *All this, I assure you, is heady stuff for a kid from Nebraska who grew up around his dad's gas station.*

*Now, what have I learned? First, plan your retirement well. The first necessity, plainly, is that you be able to afford this good time of your life. Then, when you can afford it, do not retire. That's right, don't retire. Instead, just change jobs, or occupations. Pick a second career. Because, once you can effort to retire, your nine-to-five work becomes like a hobby. For us older guys, there's no greater feeling in the world.* ◆

# Not Everyone Can Write
## a Best-selling Book

The choosing and crafting of a second career is hard work. It begins in most instances with a probing self-examination. What do I want to do with my second life? What skills, talents do I have to offer the marketplace? For many senior men, the recommended first step is in the direction of a career counselor.

I chose Robin Sheerer of Chicago. When I first asked this University of Chicago graduate and holder of a Master's degree why she considered herself an expert, she answered, "Because I've been a social worker, a psychotherapist, school teacher, waitress, and then, at age 37, I went through the difficult, painful process of self-discovery myself. I read, I studied, I questioned, and finally, I decided to open my own counseling business." In other words, Robin Sheerer has been there, done that. Now, she has acquired that most valuable counseling tool, life experience.

What wisdom does she have to pass along to older men in search of a second career, or who have been forced too soon from their jobs and are at loose ends? Her answer is unequivocal. "Get professional help." She adds that the "process of self-examination is just too hard a process to go through on your own."

Sheerer is firm in her belief that the road to discovery begins with self-knowledge. She says, "You must ask yourself, again and again, 'Hey, what do I really want with my life? What makes me happy?'" Next, you ask, "What talent do I have to match the needs of an ever-changing marketplace?"

Sheerer encourages her older clients by telling them they have experience and perspective, they have contacts, maturity, and the ability to commit. All are very marketable qualities, she explains. Further, she tells clients to "get passionate about something you genuinely want to do. No one wants to hire you to do something you're not eager to accomplish."

Work for us men doesn't have to stop, not if we're creative, resolute, tenacious, and won't take negative nonsense as the last word on the thorny, complex subject of retirement. Work in all forms—manual and mental, paid and unpaid—has long been the focus of us males. As author Alex Comfort said, "Work is the natural antidote to unhappiness."

Good luck in your quest after a second or third career. Remember, we do not allow aimless drifters or woolly-headed wanderers in the select and proud Outrageous Older Men's Club. ◆

# CHAPTER SEVENTEEN

# Volunteers

## GET TOO LITTLE CREDIT

*"The majority of Americans 55 and older are active, vital, and in good health. And the value of their contribution to society has been grossly underestimated."*

—Scott A. Bass, Ph.D., director, University of Massachusetts Gerontology Institute

Every week day, from Maine to California, some 500,000 older adults, people like you and me, work little miracles simply by giving of themselves. We call them volunteers, solid, well-meaning women and men going out into their communities to help people in need. Moreover, these selfless folks, with their white hair, thick waists, and sensible shoes, are but one part of the federal government's little-known and undervalued volunteer outreach movement. They earn next to no money, but profit isn't their motivation.

Who, you ask, are these unsung contributors, these foot soldiers on the front lines of hard times? They are volunteers in Foster Grandparents, perhaps the best-known of the many government programs. They are tutors for troubled or abused kids, van drivers for those who cannot drive, or visitors to shut-ins. They are caregivers for dying infants, helpers in senior centers and hospitals. They are teachers of the illiterate.

They serve, quietly if not anonymously, wherever they are needed. A number have written to my syndicated column, oftentimes simply to voice their gratitude for being able to contribute and, as they put it, "to give something back."

"It is satisfying to know that you help someone every day," writes one correspondent from Adrian, MI. "You forget about all your problems, your aches, your pains, for at least four hours a day."

My writer-friend was referring, specifically, to her role as a Foster Grandparent for more than one child. Each morning, she explained, she reports to an intermediate school where they teach children from kindergarten through sixth grade. Here, she is instructed to "just give love."

"There are so many youngsters who don't have a grandparent," she wrote, "and you know, a little extra loving and understanding does wonders for a lonesome child."

To become a Foster Grandparent, a volunteer must be at least 60 years old and have a small income, matching the federal definition of poverty. Each FGP candidate receives some 40 hours of orientation and training at the school, hospital, day care center, or other institution where he or she will serve and is paid a cash stipend, along with a travel allowance. Founded in 1965, the program is still small, but gets uniformly high marks from government critics. Harry R. Moody, Ph.D., writing in *Aging Concepts and Controversies,* says Foster Grandparents have shown how older people can be "reintegrated into society and be given meaningful roles in helping younger children."

The month of May, as you probably know, has been designated as National Older Americans month. Each year, I write a column urging readers to celebrate this time by giving to others, by volunteering. I also have challenged readers to tell me of their volunteer experiences.

"I do about 25 hours of volunteer work a week for the Gideons," writes a Californian, Carl H. Swadell. "I've been doing this for the past 30 years. It is far better than watching television, and it surely doesn't hurt my mental health."

"I help Meals-on-Wheels. Each Thursday morning, I am the muffin-maker," reports a man who quickly explained that he had survived five surgeries, and considered volunteer work "extremely beneficial to one's health."

Among the most unusual volunteers I've encountered is Olan Turner champion designer and flier of stunt kites. His wife, Bernice B. Turner, first wrote me from Brigantine, NJ, explaining her retired husband "has been actively sharing with children the exciting story of kites."

"The enthusiasm of the children is worth all the hours we spend making kites for kids," she said. "Hundreds of kites are painstakingly cut out by Olan to give pleasure to others. Suffice it to say our advice to people is not 'Go fly a kite,' but instead 'Come fly a kite.'" Mrs. Turner made plain in a phone conversation that Olan Turner kites, which are given to any kid who asks for one, are not ordinary paper-and-string jobs. Rather, they are stunt-flying kites operated by two powerful flying lines. A number of the Turner high-fliers have received awards at the Smithsonian Kite Festival in Washington, D.C.

I like this story, in part because no one asked the Turners, both past 70 now, to become volunteer kite people. Secondly, I celebrate their nonconformist contributions because they are intergenerational. We shall never change the negative perception of older adults until we persuade children and adolescents that we're okay people.

How many senior adults actually volunteer? The American Association of Retired Persons, with a membership of close to 40 million, believes that 45 percent of its membership does some volunteering. The Commonwealth Fund of New York reports that 38 million senior adults—approximately 70 percent of those 55 and older—volunteer time and talent to hundreds of non profit organizations. This total included individual caregivers who, in truth, are helping society.

Speaking for the Fund, Thomas Maloney said, "We've been saying these greedy geezers have been sitting on the beach, and helping out occasionally." That's an incorrect and mistaken concept, Maloney said, because "older Americans are valuable resources, rather than leisured and consuming retirees." The report called seniors a "great, overlooked national resource."

The Commonwealth survey, commissioned in 1991, further learned that men play a bigger role as volunteers and caregivers than they usually are given credit for (they volunteer at about the same rate as women), and, surprisingly, those in the 75-plus cohort "continue to be active volunteers."

If you're willing to do some volunteer work, yet you're not sure what group is right for you, consider these points.

Think of yourself as a job seeker. Ask yourself, "Honestly, what do I want to do?" For example, do you want to take advantage of your years on the job and continue in that line of work? Or would you rather break new ground and join an agency that takes you into a completely different field? Do you want to work with people? Would you be more comfortable working behind the scenes, perhaps repairing bikes or hospital wheelchairs? Do you enjoy working with young people? This self-inventory should help you make your choice.

Now, think about location. How far are you willing to travel? Obviously, if you don't want to spend time in an automobile, then Meals-on-Wheels should not be your choice. Some volunteers eagerly look for foreign travel and, therefore, the Peace Corps is a favorite. The Corps has some 7,000 volunteers serving two-year assignments in 94 countries. Ten percent of the Corps is age 50 and older, with a number in their mid-to-late 70s.

Think about what excites you. Most longtime volunteers will tell you how much they care about their volunteer work, that they feel a commitment to their group or organization. They speak in glowing terms of how "These people truly care about the work."

After you've narrowed the field, you're ready to play reporter. Take your pad and pencil and question all the volunteers you know. Compare their interests with yours. You may want to start this exercise with people you already trust, volunteers in your church or temple, your college or university, a community group that once helped you, such as the Red Cross, a senior center, an AARP chapter.

Please understand two things: First and foremost, you are needed! Budget cuts by government agencies and the business community mean that the volunteer sector has more challenges—and burdens. Secondly, it is not an easy assignment to find the right niche in the volunteer world. Know in advance that some organizations will ignore you. Others will want more time than you choose to give. A few will say, "We can't use your skills."

When I moved to Georgia from New Jersey, I rushed to volunteer with the Atlanta chapter of the Alzheimer's Association. I pledged to give them a professional looking newsletter. After five months, I realized this wasn't what they wanted or perhaps needed. I seemed out of my element and, without meaning to, was writing and editing in a politically incorrect manner, by their way of thinking. Quietly, I dropped out—without a ripple of regret on their part. Lesson learned: beware of office politics, the hydra-headed monster that exists wherever more than two people gather.

But I persevered and found another volunteer home. You do the same and, over time, you'll make your match. You can then say, "I've gained the chance to stand *in* life—not outside it. I'm continuing to keep my mind busy, even challenged. I'm determined to remain an interesting and engaged person, for I am living the *outrageous* life."

Lastly, here's a quote to copy and stick on your refrigerator or bulletin board. It underscores the value of senior volunteers. It's from Marc Freedman, vice president of a social policy research organization in Philadelphia.

"America today possesses not only the largest, best-educated and most vigorous collection of older adults in our history, but it is the fastest growing. In fact, the senior population may represent the country's only increasing natural resource."

And, every last one—including you—is a potential volunteer for good.

# These groups will help you find volunteer work:

**The AARP Volunteer Talent Bank** matches volunteers with local opportunities. Write AARP Volunteer Talent Bank, 601 E St. NW, Washington, DC 20049.

**The Points of Light Foundation** has 500 centers that provide information on local opportunities to volunteers. Call (800) 59 LIGHT for a referral to the nearest volunteer center.

**Foster Grandparent Program,** c/o "Senior Corps," 1100 Vermont Avenue, NW, Washington, DC 20525. This program matches volunteers over age 60 with disabled or troubled children.

**Habitat for Humanity,** Habitat and Church Streets, Americus, GA 31709 builds homes with help from low-income residents in the United States, Canada, and South Africa. ◆

# A Clear Call to Action

*"The percentage of men over 50 in the labor force
has diminished to its lowest point in American history."*
—from a report entitled "The Human Resource Potential
of Americans Over 50," published by John P. Wiley & Sons

They are able and fit. They are intelligent. They're also bored out of their minds. They are idled men in their 50s, 60s, 70s and 80s—and you'll find them on benches or in coffee shops all across the sunbelt of the United States. Forced retirement and downsizing play a large part in their idleness, in the boredom on their faces, and the angst in their souls.

At the same time, too many adolescent males have no father figure and next to no contact with older adults. They have no proper understanding of what it is to be older and slower, yet wiser. These young males surely could profit from hearing a firm voice explaining that drugs and guns do not constitute a lifestyle, that they do not "make a man," and that any death diminishes us all.

Pete Hamill, an author and journalist, has suggested that our country open the ranks of our armed forces to senior enlistments and allow mature men and women, if they choose, to volunteer for a period of six months to one year in an advisory or mentor-like capacity. In this way, Hamill says, we could help address the dual problems of idled older people and anchorless younger people.

"Many older Americans are possessed of a singular quality that is almost entirely absent among many young people," Hamill states. "It used to be called wisdom."

A Navy veteran, Hamill first proposed the enlistment concept when I was editor of *50 Plus* magazine and he was a freelance writer. He recalled how older men had "fought at Anzio and Tarawa, survived a depression and a great war. . . and if this country is to be truly decent, then young and old must get to know each other, on a basis of respect.

"There are many ways to bring the generations together, but senior enlistments might be the best," he wrote in a forceful essay for my magazine. In his scenario, Hamill sees an Army or Air Force barracks filled at evening time. There's a guy with a small paunch and a fringe of white hair sitting on his foot locker and all about him are young men in fatigues, questioning, probing, laughing, and learning.

Hamill's point, I submit, is clear—as a nation we need to mentor our young people and make better and fuller use of our seniors. Writing in *USA Today,* Michael

Gartner, former head of NBC/TV, said "We don't bring the old people to our high schools as living history. We don't ask them to fill in one day a week at this job or that. The healthy old are a great potential for the nation. Yet we don't tap those skills or probe those brains. We have no plan for them."

The senior enlistment concept is a plan that merits consideration both at the Pentagon and, quite possibly, inside the councils of the American Association of Retired Persons. Unquestionably, the support of AARP would command attention on Capitol Hill, where the Hamill proposal merits a full and fair hearing. ◆

# CHAPTER EIGHTEEN

# Are You Ready

## FOR THE WAR BETWEEN THE AGES?

*"The Social Security system alone costs most younger Americans more than one out of every seven dollars they earn. Not only do the young support the old—regardless of need—but the ranks of the old have never been larger."*

—Philip Longman

I t's time to introduce the one issue that, more than any other, makes old blood boil quicker, stronger, longer. I refer to entitlements, that Washington word used to describe federal programs which are a part of the national budget. Social Security and Medicare are entitlements. Under law, these entitlements mean money in the pockets of senior Americans.

Taken together, Social Security and Medicare have lifted millions of those 65 and older out of poverty and, in many cases, affords relative comfort. Every month I cash a Social Security check for $1,200, and throw a salute at the American flag in front of my post office. I'm among the lucky ones—my check pays the mortgage.

For millions, their check means far more to them than mine does. Before Social Security, these men and women chose between an evening meal or their medicines, or they decided to heat the apartment or have a hot meal with dessert. Today, after the third of the month, they can cash that beneficent, salmon-colored check and generally choose both options A and B.

But storm clouds are building. Forces are at work to toughen the laws surrounding the entitlements because the baby boomers are coming, all seventy-eight million of them. The advance boomers have turned 50, so age 65 is just over the next rise. Scare headlines demand to know if Social Security and Medicare are headed toward collapse. Meanwhile, pollsters report that when they interview boomers, only a minority expect to ever collect a Social Security check.

Some observers scoff at the gloomy forecasts. For one, the American Association of Retired Persons denies there is a crisis and argues we have ample time to address the situation. Yet Alan Greenspan, chairman of the Federal Reserve and the former chairman of a national commission on Social Security, urges Congress to address potential financing shortfalls now. "If we procrastinate too long, the adjustments could be truly wrenching," he told a Senate Social Security Task Force. "We owe it to those who will retire after the turn of the century to be given sufficient advance notice, to make what alterations in retirement planning may be required."

I hope I'm wrong, but I believe the United States is on the cusp of a potentially combustible social revolution, one which will engage most thinking Americans during the next ten years. We will be required to decide, and then legislate accordingly, what it means to be old in the United States, what is owed to older adults, what sacrifices we expect from them, and how we as a nation equitably divide up our limited entitlement pie.

This controversy is not new. In *King Lear,* there is talk of generosity toward the elderly leading to a mortgaging of "our children's future." Shakespeare also declared, "The policy and reverence of age makes the world bitter to the best of times / Keeps our fortunes from us till our oldness cannot relish them." Psychiatrist Daniel Callahan, director of the influential Hastings Center of Rye, NY, has said, "Taking care of the elderly is an endless open frontier." Plainly, the battle is joined.

Three confounding factors influence the controversy over entitlements. Each has the potential for great impact upon the nation's future. First, our staggering national deficit, a burden compiled by past and present generations, must one day be paid by future generations. Second, statistics have pointed out, over and over again, that our children—as a group—are poorer than the elderly. And third, there is the presumption that too many older Americans live too well, thanks to their powerful lobby groups and their insatiable appetites for the proverbial free lunch. These leisure driven older Americans are often categorized as "greedy geezers."

I am not going to do your thinking for you on these issues. I shall, however, call your attention to this group of facts.

1. In an essay called "Generational Equity and the New Victim Blaming," Meredith Minkler points out that the "myth of a homogenized and financially secure elderly population breaks down when the figures are disaggregated and the diversity of the elderly is taken into account."

2. Close to one-third of all African-American elders live below the federal poverty line.

3. The oldest of the old—age 85 and older—have extremely

high rates of poverty and this population is expected to double from 2.5 million to 5 million by the year 2000. Women represent the majority of this population.

4. Out-of-pocket expenses for Medicare continue to grow. According to Minkler, the charges are more than three times greater for older Americans than for other age groups.

One of the most articulate and persistent critics of Social Security's *status quo* is Peter G. Peterson, a wealthy businessman and founding president of the bipartisan Concord Coalition. "I do not believe it is un-American to suggest we live in a finite world, that some desires can't be satisfied," Peterson has said, and "the economic implications of America's aging population over the next several decades will dwarf, in sheer dollars, any other issue one might name."

In his controversial book, *Will America Grow Up Before It Grows Old?*, Peterson wrote, "Unlike the United States, other countries are unencumbered by the illusion their people have some sort of an inalienable right to live out the last third of their adult life in subsidized leisure."

Peterson is a fiscal expert, someone who has made a fortune through investment counseling. He has called for a Social Security means test (those earning $40,000 or less per year would be exempt), raising the eligibility age to 70, and the creation of a mandatory savings plan. His contention is that he wants to spare our grandchildren from unconscionable economic burdens. In a speech before a middle-class retirement audience, Peterson showed pictures of his grandchildren. "I explained my concerns about their future and the world they would inherit," he writes. "I reminded the retirees how much of our national affluence today rests on the willingness we had to make collective sacrifices during the Great Depression and World War II."

Millionaire Pete Peterson then asked the men and women

how many would be willing to sacrifice a share of their federal benefits "in order to ease the burden on younger generations." Everyone in the room held up a hand, one more demonstration of the volunteer spirit of most older Americans.

Now what is your individual role in this drama? Let me suggest that self-interest, along with your duties as a citizen, dictate you should play an active part in the entitlements debate. Here are a few suggestions to get you started.

- Begin by being well-informed. Read your newspapers, your news magazines, and then spend a morning at your local library. Through the years, Social Security has been a favorite topic for reviews and histories so there will be a lot of background information on your library's shelves. Look for articles by Robert J. Myers. He was the chief actuary for the Social Security Administration and later served as deputy commissioner of the agency. He is one of the most knowledgeable of the experts. Incidentally, he believes the Peterson book includes many factual errors.

- Get active. If you're not already a member, check your local phone directory for the nearest chapter of the American Association of Retired Persons—and join. Or, if you prefer a smaller organization, check into the National Committee to Preserve Social Security and Medicare. Their address is: 2000 K Street NW, Suite 800, Washington, D.C. 20006. Both groups lobby hard on Capitol Hill in support of senior Americans.

- Make your viewpoint known by writing your congressional representative and senators. Most Americans regard this exercise as a waste of time. I don't. At the very least, you'll feel better for making the effort. If you balk at this assignment, then write your hometown newspaper or television station. Emphasize the facts and figures you've uncovered from personal research. You may get published or, better still, interviewed. Many newspapers are looking for pieces for their op-ed (opposite the editorials) page.

Peterson's Concord Coalition and other organizations predict that we're headed for a generational conflict that will pit American against American in a way our nation has never known. Candidly, I view such statements as horse feathers, purely inflammatory rhetoric designed to capture public attention and headlines. I prefer the moderate view voiced by Generations United which believes the struggles of one age group are the struggles of all. This Washington-based organization represents 100 different groups, all working to keep harmony and cooperation at the forefront as the American people seek to address a variety of fiscal, social, and civic dilemmas.

To contact Generations Unlimited, write them at 440 First Street, NW, Washington, D.C. 20001-2085. Their telephone number is (202) 638-2952 and E-mail can be sent to: GU@CWLA.org. Members get a quarterly newsletter and public policy information. There's also an annual meeting.

I think we're going to have earnest, even angry, debate over these issues. Fiery speeches and political posturing will fuel the public drama. We are an ageist society but when push comes to shove, we take care of our older parents, grandparents, and neighbors. Meredith Minkler reminds us that Louis Harris and Associates have conducted twenty national surveys and none of them support the idea of a coming intergenerational conflict.

To be absolutely certain your future is going to be secure and the third of the month will still put a smile on your face, pick up your feet, join the campaign of your choice, and begin to get downright outrageous.

# CHAPTER NINETEEN

# On Becoming

*"The time comes, for most of us, when we have to consider—for ourselves or someone we love—those awful places, those terrible, necessary institutions, those nursing homes. . . Standing apart, almost parenthetically removed from its environment, the nursing home becomes a kind of tribal village, a place of misfits. . . designed for people who have no other place to go, no other place to be. . . "*

—Sallie Tisdale, author of
*Harvest Moon, Portrait of a Nursing Home*

In a neighborhood close to your home, the phone will ring late tonight inside a darkened bedroom. An anxious female voice will announce, "It's Dad. He's fallen." The older brother to the woman making this emergency call instinctively asks if their father is all right.

The hesitant answer is, "He's broken his hip. . . he's in a lot of pain." Then, following a pause, "He's going to need a lot of help."

With this episode, another American family is drawn inexorably, into the great, ever-widening circle of caregivers. Additionally, another older adult is started down the long road of rehabilitation, one which ends most times with a nursing home stay. Here, alone and troubled, surrounded by unfamiliar, often threatening sights and smells, the patient struggles to adjust—to retain some semblance of control over his or her life. The truth is, he can succeed only if he has well-informed, aggressive advocates.

"Dad seems so vulnerable—so confused—in the nursing home. I want to help," say this patriarch's adult children. "But how?" The answer to that inquiry is: become his advocate!

Advocate is from the Latin word *advocare* and it means to call, summon, to give voice! We are all natural advocates. Every day we advocate on behalf of our own best interests, as well as those of our family and friends. Some of us just work at it a little longer, perhaps a little harder, and occasionally at higher decibels.

Permit me to describe how an average citizen became, overnight, an outraged advocate. Our narrative begins in a north Georgia nursing home where a resident, a widower in his mature 80s, is tied to an easy chair. A curious visitor asks, "Why the restraint?"

"It's for his own good," said a nurse, and then the nursing home's administrator added, "He could fall, you know."

At this point, the visitor, dissatisfied with this explanation, began his own quiet inquiry into nursing home restraints. By asking questions and reading, he learned the following:

- The resident in question was frail, yet had never fallen.

- Despite the fact that restraints are prohibited by federal law, restraints and vests, or ties, continue to be used in nursing homes throughout the United States.

- Specialists explain that these restraints, in too many cases, are arbitrarily assigned, in part because they make life simpler for nursing home staff.

- One more melancholy, and outrageous, fact: restraints kill people. They kill emotionally and physically, oftentimes by strangulation.

The nursing home resident in this instance was a north Georgia farmer, J.R. Still, my wife's late grandfather. From the time I first found him restrained, I became a voice of outrage, raised often in opposition to the demeaning, largely unnecessary binding of institutionalized, generally helpless, elderly men and women.

"Among other things, the use of restraints teaches helplessness," explained Margaret Flint, a lawyer with the Brookdale Center on Aging in New York City and an expert on the problem. We had met for lunch and she told me that at that time, maybe half the people in nursing homes throughout New York were in some form of restraint, either by being tied down or through drugs.

"It doesn't have to be," she said. "Frankly, I find the whole idea appalling." (Please note, this interview took place in 1987 and the situation in New York has significantly improved, thanks to advocacy.)

Meanwhile, my continuing education on restraints led me next to the National Citizens' Coalition for Nursing Home Reform (NCCNHR) in Washington, D.C., and to Sarah Greene Burger, R.N. This knowledgeable advocate, a former nursing home employee and frequent writer on nursing home abuses and indignities, said, "We have new information that says it's actually safer *not* to use restraints. Our research shows that people die in restraints all the time—not only because of the symptoms that develop from being immobilized, but from being strangled."

For several years now, I have been a persistent advocate and a veritable grouch, carping, wailing, and pointing fingers at the homes where restrained residents, bound in vests and ties, are too frequent. My advocacy has been met at times with anger and resentment. Shrill rejoinders have come from administrators, practical nurses, health aides, and even family members—all of whom have suggested that I am, at best, ignorant and, at worst, smoking an illegal weed.

Today, as the good fight continues, I refer naysayers and critics to *Nursing Homes: Getting Good Care There,* a consumer book published by the NCCNHR. Chapter five in this eminently readable softcover guide is entitled "Good Care Is Restraint-Free." These two sentences jump out at you from the opening page:

"Research has shown that restraints are dangerous and destructive. . . Professional caregivers have learned how to eliminate restraints by studying the care of residents in other countries."

Sarah Burger, whom I today regard as a professional pal, is one of four authors behind *Good Care.* This quartet of women, all veterans of the nursing home wars, makes a profound statement about good care—the time you spend finding a nursing home for your father, or mother, or great aunt, is time well spent. However, once that reluctant placement is made, your job—as caregiver and advocate—truly begins. In other words, from that day forward, you are *on duty*, with full responsibility for that loved person's welfare and contentment. Maybe your first job, after becoming familiar with the home and its staff, is to join the Residents Council. These women and men meet regularly and serve as a sounding board, a watchdog, and when needed, as liaison to the state ombudsman. If there is no council in place, organize one. After all, that's what outrageous, and courageous, older men do—they advocate effectively.

Finally, my hat comes off to salute those men who, by the hundreds of thousands, are currently caregivers to aged parents or other relatives. This clearly is a new brand of *outrageousness*, the positive kind, the kind that says "I care. . . no matter the cost."

# Help Needed to Feed Nursing Home Residents

Would you believe that nursing home residents are starving to death, not from lack of food but because they're not being properly fed? I didn't—not until I read a blistering report to the United States Senate's Special Committee on Aging.

Jeanie Kayser-Jones, Ph.D., of the University of California, San Francisco, told the senators that "malnutrition is a common, potentially serious, yet frequently undetected and often untreated problem in longterm care institutions."

To put a face and personality on this shameful national dilemma, the researcher spoke of a woman of 89, a stroke victim, who has no family and no visitors—and, therefore, no advocate. "Imagine for a moment that you are this woman," Kayser-Jones began. "You have some memory loss, but you are able to state your wishes and make decisions regarding your care. You can feed yourself if someone sets up the tray, cuts your meat, and positions you comfortably."

Mealtime, however, is invariably troublesome because you, like a majority of other residents, also suffer from hand tremor, you have only three remaining teeth, you have stomach pain, and in just nine months have lost 28 pounds from your normal weight of 128. Additionally, you suffer from dysphagia, meaning you have trouble swallowing your food.

Clearly, this handicapped patient needs help—a lot of help—with her feeding. Yet, the nursing aides have only minutes, too few minutes, in which to feed too many patients.

This is how Dr. Kayser-Jones summed up the situation. "When we think of people going to bed hungry, many of us tend to think of developing countries. . . or people in North Korea. Most of us would not believe that in some American homes people also go to bed hungry, not because food is unavailable to them, but because, among other factors, no one takes the time to feed them.

"Based on our data," added the investigator who has spent twenty years studying the problem, "I believe that what is defined as an eating problem is in fact often a staffing problem."

Now, why do I choose to highlight this unhappy condition? Because it cries out for advocates and volunteers. I refer to responsible older men with a sense of outrage, seniors who are willing to march into nursing homes in their community and say, for openers, "Hey, is there someone who's waiting to be fed?"

Can a society call itself civilized if it does not provide sensitive, humane quality care to elderly people during the last days of their lives? That is the question the California doctor left with the senators when her meticulously researched, eloquent presentation was complete.

The next move is up to us.

You may contact the **National Citizens Coalition for Nursing Home Reform** by writing them at 1224 M Street, NW (Suite 301), Washington, D.C. 20005. Their phone number is (202) 332-2275. This organization is a consistent provider of relevant information. ◆

# CHAPTER TWENTY

# Making

## THE SYSTEM WORK FOR YOU

*"Most people are unaware there is such a
thing as the Aging Network."*

—The New York Times

Your widowed father-in-law, age 87 and diabetic, is moving in with you and your wife. Up and down the block, you find neighbors clucking and feeling sorry about your future. "You're going to need home care," they say. "Finding responsible and reasonable people—well, that's the name of the game."

One of your neighbors is a retired lawyer. He reads everything and now he takes you aside. "Do you know about the Older Americans Act?" he asks. Then he explains how this service network is all paid for with your tax dollars. But it's up to you to make the support programs function for your family.

Later, in the library, you read that the Older Americans Act was passed in 1965 under President Lyndon Johnson and that it has the ambitious goal of "assuring the well-being of the elderly." The law established the primary sources of human and social services for all older Americans. These services include senior centers, nutrition or meal programs, unemployment assistance, the ombudsman program for nursing homes, and others. The combined services provided under the OAA have a budget of approximately $1 billion.

The act also created several agencies for accomplishing specific goals at the federal, state, and local levels, including the federal Administration on Aging (AoA), state units on aging, and locally based Area Agencies on Aging. Take out your local phone directory and see what your community or county offers in the way of aging services.

In many locales, you need only one telephone number to tap into this network for aging Americans. For example, if you live in Palo Alto, CA, one call to the Senior Coordinating Council,—(415) 326-5362—will get you started. This private, non profit group not only gives caregiving advice, but also offers home-repair and housekeeping assistance, transportation, information on adult day care and respite care, Medicare counseling, tax return preparation, volunteer activities, seasonal flu shots, and other health care. Moreover, the Council serves daily meals, and even offers computer classes.

The entire roster of senior services offered by this Senior Coordinating Council requires thirty-three lines in the local phone book. Yet, in a city with more than 26,000 persons 60 years and older, fewer than 6,000 individuals take advantage of these free or low-cost services in any given year. Why so few?

"The majority don't know we're here," answers Kathleen Gwynn, who was president and CEO of the council when I interviewed her. The council operates with more than a $2 million budget and its center is situated in the shadow of the prestigious, affluent Stanford University community.

Gwynn offers other possible reasons for her agency being underutilized. "Denial. They [seniors] don't want to think of themselves as growing older. Or, they're reluctant to ask an agency—a stranger to them—for help. Maybe they have other support systems, a church or their own family. . . "

In Washington, Nancy Gurshe, an assistant director of the Administration on Aging, the umbrella organization overseeing the Area Agencies on Aging (AAoA) in all 50 states, said flatly, "People still don't know about us. As a result, many of our programs—good programs, too—are underused."

Another misconception is, the aging network serves only people who have no money. Not true. Senior services are open to all, and most don't charge a nickel. Others are based on an ability to pay. However, to take advantage of them, you must tap into the system.

1. Call the Eldercare Locator at (800) 677-1116 for the name and phone number of the agency nearest you.

2. Next, telephone the number and explain your needs.

3. Pick and choose from its menu of offerings in health, employment, education, nutrition, and social services that will help you.

No two agencies offer exactly the same array of services because programs are structured to meet each community's needs, but few agencies turn people away simply on the basis of residence. Computer classes at the Palo Alto center, for instance, are attended by residents of neighboring Menlo Park, Los Altos, and Mountain View, even though these communities have their own centers.

Perhaps the most important service provided by these local area agencies is the one called client assessment. This consists of an interview with a social worker, followed by health examination which typically includes a blood pressure reading, vision and hearing tests, a check for diabetes, heart disease, and the recording of a complete medical history. The purpose is to determine the older adult's status and his or her needs. Usually, these exams are performed on behalf of an adult caregiver who is looking after an aging parent. An analysis of this interview and the exams leads to a care management plan developed by a social worker with the understanding it will be carried out by the caregiver.

We began this chapter with mention of a father-in-law who was about to move into your home. If a similar situation does happen to you, please reach out for the professional help you'll need in order to properly serve your patient and retain some semblance of normalcy in your marriage and homelife. Now that you're better informed, you're ready to tackle this challenge, one that most of us will know at some point.

For me, the moment came when my ailing mother, happy in her south Florida condominium, was diagnosed with emphysema *and* lung cancer. A New York woman born and bred, straight out of the flapper era, Martha Quitzau Lindeman had smoked cigarettes from the time she was a rebellious teen, and no force on earth could dissuade her from this self-destructive behavior, certainly not at the age of 79. My three children and I accepted and loved her for who she was. Marvelous Martha's charm, as well as her worldly wise qualities, are at the core of the loving stories that we still tell about her whenever we're together. Since I was busy in New York editing *50 Plus* magazine at that time, I hired a geriatric case manager to oversee my mother's care. In addition, my son Paul, who was a medical student at the University of Miami, looked after her. Working as a team, we saw to it that she was as comfortable and content as circumstances allowed.

Her anticipated death came late one summer night, just days

after Dr. Paul Lindeman graduated. By all accounts, the death was peaceful and dignified. She was at home with a caregiver at her bedside. Moreover, the passing was so like stoical, all-loving Martha. We are convinced she simply hadn't wanted to rain on Paul's parade so she waited until after he crossed the stage, medical diploma in hand.

As I write this, it's been more than a decade since she died and I still can't bring myself to take her phone card from my Rolodex. I miss her today, even as I lament that I wasn't holding her hand in those final hours. My consolation is that the family, with the essential and compassionate help of our Florida care manager, did the right thing for her.

If you can afford to hire a professional care manager, it is the preferred way to travel. Make good use as well of the social support system for all aging Americans.

> If you have difficulty finding your state's area agency on aging, simply call the **Eldercare Locator** at: (800) 617-1116.

# CHAPTER TWENTY ONE

# Is the Open Road

## FOR YOU?

*"He that travels much knows much."*

—Thomas Fuller, M.D.

Whether you call them Snowbirds or Full-timers, you had better watch their dust, because these people are ready to roll. Late fall is their big time of the year, the time when they gas up and head for the open road. The time when they chase the sun.

"If I never see snow again, it will suit me fine," they'll tell you and, given half a chance, launch into tales of nasty Chicago winters or blizzards in Minnesota.

These outrageous types are retirees, popularly known as RVers, or owners of recreational vehicles. They are men and women primed for the long haul with only a post office box for an address. Turn up your nose or laugh if you choose, but they are the nation's current nomads, a growing tribe of committed wanderers who represent a new American subculture, along with an undervalued economy.

While there is no reliable count on the total number living and traveling in RVs, the Family Motor Coach Association believes 1.5 million is a reliable estimate. Moreover, it is said the open-roaders own $50 billion worth of trailers and motor homes. A motor home, incidentally, is a self-propelled vehicle that is also a home. A mobile home, which doesn't move much in spite of its name, is an entirely different critter.

Here's some tips on how to spot RV full-timers. They all have gray or white hair and are 50 years old or older. In fact, many are in their 70s. Generally, there are two people to an RV, a husband and wife. A few singles are out there, and some pairs of the same gender, women-friends mostly. There are no children, except for an occasional grandchild who may be playing hooky from school.

A full-timer can be almost anyone—a retired medical doctor or lawyer, a production line worker, military retiree, school teacher, or small business owner. One RVer reports, "In every camp I've visited, you'll find at least several computers along with one absolute whiz willing to show off his or her computer prowess."

Their RV equipment is almost always well kept, and can be luxurious. The term "roughing it" doesn't apply here. One couple I know travels in air-conditioned comfort, making good use of their side-by-side refrigerator/freezer/stove as well as their microwave and television. They sleep in a queen-sized bed, and are surrounded by what they describe as "solid, attractive furniture."

If you spend time around these road regulars, you'll notice they have routines, a way of sharing tasks. For example, Mom has a system of hand signals that she uses to direct Dad while he backs the trailer into the campsite. They go for brisk walks or bicycle rides after supper. They always act with a relaxed confidence and they're content with their new lifestyle.

Meanwhile the stay-at-home types, a category in which I

include myself, boast of our gardens or favorite chair and question how RVers are able to give up the longtime comforts of home for back roads, highways, and one-nighters in roadside camps. Isn't life on the road like being a perpetual Boy Scout or Campfire girl?

"The RV life requires more nerve and commitment than a lot of people are willing to risk," answers Jim Jordan, 71, speaking for his wife Betty, as well. For some seven years, the Jordans have been RVers and when we got together by telephone, the couple was parked in Space 3-286 in a camp outside Tucson, AZ. The Jordans agreed to answer my questions, including the obligatory "Why do you do it?"

I doubt that there is one single answer behind the decision to be an RVer, but Jim Jordan, whose work life began when he was 12, explained his decision this way. "Traveling as we do, you leave behind a phone that constantly rings. You manage to avoid salespeople at your door, that barking dog or grouchy neighbor down the block, not to mention yard work and real estate taxes.

"We sold our home, bought an RV, and took off. Suddenly, or so it seemed, our 'home' was wherever our RV was parked. We've been in all the lower forty-eight states, thirty of them more than once. We never have regretted our decision.

"To us, the opportunities seem endless. With an RV, you set your own schedule, go where you want, when you want. Do you enjoy art galleries? Try the one at Albuquerque, or at Santa Fe, Tulsa, Sedona, AZ, or the National Gallery in Washington. I can tell you that it's exciting to look over the shoulder of a scientist excavating fossils in the Dakotas or Utah. Have you taken the ferry to Victoria to see the beautiful gardens? Have you walked through Williamsburg, or maybe Knotts Berry Farm?

"If you're a golfer, why not play Palm Springs or Virginia Beach? I mean off-season, when it isn't so crowded. For those who fish, how about flipping a fly into a beautiful, winding stream in Colorado, with no one else in sight for maybe half a mile?"

For her part, Betty Jordan explained that, like most Americans, she and Jim had wanted an active, even adventurous retirement—and so she convinced her husband, the workaholic, that "we had better get to it, and do it now while we're physically able."

"Full-timers have something in common," Jim continued. "We all left familiar surroundings to 'see the world.' We're willing now to share something of ourselves. And, most important of all, RVers are willing to help others in need.

"Most of us look to meet new people, and possibly develop friendships—friendships that may, or may not, last."

Listening to Jim and Betty Jordan, I was reminded of the late Charles Kuralt, that brilliant essayist for CBS-TV who made his mark as the *On The Road* correspondent. Called by *Time* magazine "the laureate of the common man," Kuralt once said "I come from wandering tribes. I always wondered where the roads went."

Kuralt logged more than one million miles in his motor home over more than 20 years and, in his 1990 autobiography, remembered how "the front pages were full of selfishness, arrogance and hostility to others. [But] the back roads were another country. . . I had to revise my conception of the people who lived in the country—the people I met seemed neighborly and humane. I didn't have to worry about finding stories any longer. They found me."

That's the way it is with the Kuralts, the Jordans, and all the other over-the-road travelers who are patient, perceptive, and open to new experiences. The stories naturally seem to find them.

If you like new stories, if you're fond of new places, and have the least bit of wanderlust, you might want to consider the life of the RVer. You can be sure of this—it's one outrageous way to get from here to there.

# Before You Go

I f you decide to purchase a recreational vehicle, you must become an aware, educated consumer first. My RV connection, Jim Jordan, offers this advice. "Shop for a dealership as aggressively as you shop for the vehicle. Meaning, you need to find a good one. Search out and talk to the customers—at least several of them—of this dealer. Remember, you cannot ask too many questions.

"An ethical dealer will guide you in choosing what you really need at a price that is competitive. Then that dealer will teach you how everything works. The responsible dealer also will make certain you know how to handle the unit properly."

For reading on the subject, you might consider *Full-time RVing* by Bill and Jan Moeller, or *Survival of the Snowbirds* by Joe and Kay Peterson. Try your local library for help in locating reference materials. ◆

# Have You Ever Seen a Giraffe Born?

Helena Koenig, grandmother to five, started GrandTravel in Bethesda, MD, years ago when, as a new grandmother, she decided there was a business opportunity here. "There were trips for doctors, lawyers, Daughters of the American Revolution, insurance types, yet none for grandparents with their grandkids."

Where, I asked, do grandparents take their little darlings? "To the Grand Canyon, of course," Helena said. But also to see the castles of England and Scotland, to classical Italy, the wilderness of Alaska, Hawaii, Australia, and Kenya in far-off East Africa.

"For the animals!" Helena said, emphatically answering my question of "Why Kenya, of all places?"

This veteran of 46 years in the travel business explained how she was, in fact, selling "cultural inheritances, as well as a time of bonding." When I heard the heady price of this two-week, overseas jaunt to Kenya, I raised a skeptical eye. Koenig was prepared.

"In all probability," she began, "grandparents are going to leave money to their grandkids. This way, they all get to enjoy the trip of a lifetime—and will come away with incredible memories. That much I guarantee.

"Have you ever seen a giraffe born?" she asked. "It's the most beautiful thing in the world. Watching it struggle to walk, with those ridiculous knees. It brings tears to your eyes."

Realizing she was educating a city boy, someone who hadn't slept in a tent since he grew out of his Boy Scout uniform at age 12, Helena Koenig said, "It's not what you think. It's not hot and buggy. You travel first class, and the service truly is spectacular.

"The night skies, and the stars. . . and the quiet," she said next, with awe and wonder in her voice. "They are all part of this total experience. At times, the silence is absolute." A Kenya tour or safari accommodates up to twenty-two travelers—ten grandparents and ten grand-children plus two GrandTravel guides. The group flies into Nairobi, the Kenyan capital, to begin its trek of fourteen days and twelve nights.

The lure, of course, is the wildlife—prides of lions, ele-phants, rare bongo antelope, 300 varieties of birds (including vultures), white colobus monkeys, leopards, rhinos, herds of wildebeest, and those promised giraffes.

"If you're truly lucky," Koenig added, "you'll see a lion kill. My mouth is still open," she continued. "This is nature in the raw."

For GrandTravel information, or its 64-page, illustrated brochure describing some seventeen destinations in the United States and overseas, write **GrandTravel,** 6900 Wisconsin Avenue, Suite 706, Chevy Chase, MD 20815. Or call (800) 247-7651.

GrandTravel is not the only agency catering to grandparents and grandkids. Others include:

**American Wilderness Experience of Boulder,** CO (800) 444-0099

**Insider's Italy of Brooklyn,** NY (718) 855-3878

**Rascals in Paradise of San Francisco,** CA (415) 978-9800).◆

# OUTRAGEOUS
# *Relationships*

# CHAPTER TWENTY TWO

# Sex

## IS FOR BIRDS, BEES AND GUYS, TOO

*"Sex is part of life,
and for those fortunate enough
to be healthy and not alone,
it can last as long as life itself."*

—David B. Barasch, *Aging, An Exploration*

*"When both of you take off your glasses,
and put them on the nightstand,
everyone and everything is beautiful."*

—Myrna V., Tucson, AZ,
responding to a newspaper column on sexuality

Harant Katchadourian, Ph.D., professor of human biology at Stanford University and a popular lecturer, has these relevant things to say on the important issue of sexual performance.

"Sex in the young is fast and furious. It is ignited easily and fizzles out like fireworks. Some of us grow old, yet never outgrow this style. But men and women who grow in sexual sophistication, along with the years, can find new vistas of satisfaction.

"With the passage of time it is possible to expand sex into a different and, in some ways, richer experience. . . which amply compensates for whatever deficits are incurred."

There you have it. The lowdown from on high, teaching us that sexuality in later life, like other aspects of aging, is what we elect to make it. Regrettably, a combination of misunderstanding and lack of knowledge (in some quarters it's called ignorance) prevents many senior couples from enjoying the pleasures of sex. They fail to recognize or accept the changes that occur with the decades, and do not capitalize on the differences that can enhance—not diminish—sexual satisfaction for both partners.

Even worse, these backsliders accept as true too many fallacious and malicious notions, such as:

1. Older men and women are universally asexual.

2. Senior women are too "dried up" for good sex, while men can't maintain a decent erection or reach climax in this century.

3. Step aside, geezer! Sex is the province and playground of those with hard bodies.

Author David Barasch wrote, "Hell hath no fury like the young, confronted with the sexuality of the old." He also quotes from a William Butler Yeats poem, "You think it horrible that lust and rage / Should dance attention upon my old age. . . ."

If you don't believe that ageism and other biases are factors in this dynamic, then tune in television's Jay Leno some night. You won't have to wait long before the host of the *Tonight* show is poking fun at some older male actor, athlete, politician. Millions of viewers watching from their bedrooms are anticipating that all-American sport of demeaning and ridiculing older adults because of impotence, incontinence, or some other inadequacy.

"If older people can be persuaded that they are unsexed, then in fact they will be," concludes Barasch. This professor of psychology recalls that the famous Alfred Kinsey study of sexual behavior of 14,084 people included only 106 folks over the age of 60 and of those, only 18 were older than 70. "In itself," Barasch comments, "this speaks eloquently."

The fact is that, as the years slip by, two sets of changes occur and both have an affect on sexual arousal, sexual performance, and orgasm. Physically, the flow in our circulation system lessens and muscles relax. Since blood flow accounts for male erection and muscular contractions produce orgasm, men have more difficulty attaining, then maintaining, an erection. Further, the orgasm may be less forceful or slower to arrive.

More profound changes occur in the most responsive sex organ of all—*the mind.* Over time, the women may become more sexually aggressive, possibly because there is no longer any fear of pregnancy. Men, meanwhile, can become less aggressive. They mellow and are more willing to be led, comforted. According to Dr. Katchadourian and others, men may think less about sex, giving way to fewer sexual fantasies. (None of my 70-plus friends or acquaintances still subscribes to *Playboy* or *Penthouse.*)

Close behind the mind as an undervalued organ, are the vocal cords. Indeed, nothing enhances sexual performance like communicating your enjoyments and pleasures. (Don't neglect to add the words "please" and "thank you.") In addition, you and your partner need to talk through any problems before they reach the chronic stage, and keep in mind that love is still the greatest aphrodisiac by far.

Remember, too, that the physical and psychological changes that come with age aren't problems if you accept them and work through them in tandem. Unfortunately, too many couples push their disappointments aside, neglecting or refusing to address them. Even worse, partners place blame on each other.

Dr. Alex Comfort, author of *The Joy of Sex,* once said, "Old folks stop having sex for the same reason they stop riding a bicycle: general infirmity, thinking it looks ridiculous, no bicycle."

With the above as prologue, it's time to move from the physical side of sexuality to the emotional, or spiritual, side and introduce what is known as the "second language of sex." The queen of Q&A columnists, Ann Landers, touched a national nerve a decade ago when she posed this provocative question to her largely female following: "Would you prefer to be held closely and treated tenderly, and forget about 'the act?'"

The response was as dramatic as it was unanticipated. The doyenne of advice columnists received more than 60,000 cards and letters saying that cuddling came first. A spokeswoman for Landers said archly, "Not all were signed by women."

Dr. Robert Butler and his co-author and wife, Myrna Lewis, underscored that point in their book, *Love and Sex after 60*. "Affection, warmth, and sensuality do not have to deteriorate with age; they may, in fact, increase." Holding, touching, and hugging can be as enjoyable as aiming for some high level of sexual performance, they state, and add, "Part of the secret of learning the second language lies in learning how to give. Healthy giving involves the pleasures inherent in giving, regardless of return. The second language implies sensitivity and suggests that possibility of renewing love every day."

The brilliant novelist Gabriel Garcia Marquez, writing in *Love in the Time of Cholera*, describes a couple in their 70s as "living together long enough to know that love was always love, anytime and anywhere, but it was more solid the closer it came to death."

Indeed, no matter what the young contend, as life goes on, so does loving, and the artful making of love.

# Women Define "A Sexy Man"

What do women really want from us men? What makes for a "sexy guy" in older dudes? As the editor of *50 Plus* magazine, I believed the answers to these questions were best learned from our women readers. It was among my better decisions. Here is what we found out.

- Women want tenderness, affection, consideration, gentleness, and thoughtfulness. Warm and easy smiles also must be part of the total package of a sexy male partner.

- Women past 50 also want their men to be intelligent, and have good senses of humor.

- A surprising number of respondents mentioned cleanliness. As one woman stated, "A sexy man is one who looks, feels, and smells nice."

- Further, they described the sexy man as vibrant, dynamic, and "definitely communicative."

- Older women want men who are not afraid to show their emotions. "Sensitive to my feelings, as well as his own," wrote one woman.

- Approximately one-third of the several hundred letters said physical characteristics such as height, hair color, or color of eyes don't matter. Instead, "a sexy man has a twinkle in his eye, a quick laugh, and a lilt in his walk. He likes me, and tells me when I look good."

• In rating the sex appeal of body parts, women voted for "sparkling eyes" and "sensuous eyes." Just 8 percent said the penis was the most important body part. The eyes received a 41 percent response.

• Sixty-one percent of the women who took the time to complete our survey admitted that a man's impotence "would not affect a desire for him." One woman said "My husband looks 55, is handsome, and has a great body. In truth, he's 67 and impotent. We've never had intercourse. Despite that, he's great in bed. We have fun together sexually, and lots of potent men can't say as much. Yes, I love him, and I'm nineteen years his junior!"

• Although the majority of women said their ideal man was tall, 72 percent would have no problem dating a bald man. "Baldness is in his genes," one woman wrote. "It's not his fault." ◆

# CHAPTER TWENTY THREE

# Meeting People–

## AN ANTIDOTE TO LONELINESS

*"You are as young as your hope,*
*and as old as your despair."*

—Anonymous

I f loneliness among older adults were a corporation, it would be a "growth stock." The human condition we know as loneliness, with its attendant pain and alienation, is unarguably epidemic throughout the United States.

It's no mystery why this is so. More than half of all women over 65 are widows and that depressing proportion rises to 70 percent for women over 75. Moreover, there are between 1.5 and 2 million widowers in the country at any one time. I became a member of the fraternity of American widowers at the age of 41. If you're lucky or blessed, I hope you'll escape the searing negative experiences that come with this membership.

During my time as a widower, I read and reviewed *The Broken Heart: The Medical Consequences of Loneliness*. The premise of its author, psychologist James J. Lynch, is that "isolation and lack of companionship are the greatest unrecognized contributors to premature death." In an interview he told me, "Using white divorced males under 70 as a cohort, you find heart disease is twice as frequent—hypertension is almost triple [that of men who are in relationships]. You can see similar evidence in persons of every racial and sexual group who live alone."

But wait—we know that living alone doesn't necessarily produce loneliness. Lynch argues the two conditions oftentimes work in concert, and the resulting tune can be sour. "My solutions," Dr. Lynch announced, "are elementary. If you want to find love, you've got to give love." He further believes that as a society "We ought to attack today's myth of the independent person. There is such a thing as healthy dependency. No one is biologically independent."

With this thought as prologue, let us explore ways in which the senior man who is alone can avoid a state of loneliness by meeting new people. Repeat after me: "Every widower—indeed, every single person—needs to accept that the road to meeting someone new goes through the mind." Yes, the possibilities of meeting new people are limited almost always by your imagination and sense of daring.

In her book *How to Find Love, Sex and Intimacy after 50,* Dr. Matti Gershenfeld says, "If you still think there are no places to meet men (or women), you haven't looked in the best place of all—your mind."

The idea here is that in order to meet someone, you first have to make a commitment. Then you need to plan, plot, and scheme your way into the best possible situation so the alleged "magic" can happen. For example, I met my wife Jan when she introduced me as the speaker to a group of Women in Communications. In her remarks she made fun of me. Hours later in my motel room, I found the courage to telephone her and say "If you're not busy tonight, I'd like to meet you for a glass of sarsaparilla."

Let me offer an example of what I mean about making the effort or the commitment. I don't like cruises, but as the editor of *50 Plus* magazine, I felt obliged to try one. Wife Jan and I sailed to Mexico, Jamaica, the Cayman Islands, and back to Florida. Surrounded by hundreds of pleasant strangers, I made no new friends. I didn't care to.

But once during the Georgia Senior Olympics, I met a couple on a deserted football field where the husband was practicing his softball toss. There was a steady rain falling and the wife, with an umbrella over her head, was retrieving the hard throws as best she could. I jogged over, curious to meet this unusual pair. "Can I help out?" I offered. Later, we three talked and exchanged names and phone numbers.

In the first instance, I did nothing to clear the path to my meeting someone. Instead, I kept to myself. In the second case, I went out of my way to be friendly—purposely so. Simply put, I had wanted to engage the earnest husband-wife team.

Psychologists refer to the wallflower stage when adolescents, self-conscious about their looks, and generally insecure, hang back in social situations. They're waiting for someone to take them by the hand, to rescue them. Well, older adults go through the same sort of emotional turmoil as widowers, widows, and singles. Oftentimes women write my column saying they refuse to go to restaurants because they're invariably greeted with "Just one?"

"Older men and women frequently suffer a recurrence of adolescent jitters," psychologist Lawrence D. Simkins wrote. At singles gatherings, he added, "They find themselves waiting for someone to approach them. They truly don't know how to act."

I don't buy it. They know how to act, they're just afraid of rejection and so react with shyness, awkwardness. Well, that dog won't hunt. You've got to break through, force yourself to be aggressive, open, receptive. I'll teach you a trick. Take along a pen and a pad. Tell yourself that you're a columnist and you're writing a piece on how best to meet people. Walk across the room and say to that attractive woman you'd like to know, "Can we talk? I'm a journalist and I'd like to ask you a dozen or so questions."

If she asks "What paper are you with?" your answer should be "I'm doing research for Bard Lindeman. He's syndicated by the Chicago Tribune people."

The following are a few places where the odds of meeting someone new tilt in your favor. Good luck with your journey.

There is no safer bet than attending a family event where your best interests are well represented. Do *not* pass up any family gathering—weddings, anniversary parties, birthday celebrations, graduations, or religious services such as a bar mitzvah or First Communion. To begin, conversation will come easily. "Whose cousin did you say you were?" In addition, remind your hostess well in advance that you're open to meeting her friends. Ask to be seated in the "singles" section.

Depending upon your inclinations, you may choose to visit a piano bar (better brush up on your Cole Porter lyrics) or the public library. Both can be lively places. While at the library, ask about joining a Great Books discussion group.

Walking a sweet-natured dog is almost a guarantee that people will talk to you. Some women joggers even stop to talk with and pet my Sir Nicholas during our morning constitutionals.

Please don't turn up your nose at senior centers. Friends of mine who are regulars tell me that no single man will go unattended or unattached for long in these controlled environments.

Join a health club, go to a gym, or take up a sport. These are all surefire ways to find new faces. Weekends usually are best for this pursuit because working people as well as homebodies will be there.

A woman who was twice divorced and on the far side of 60 told Dr. Gershenfeld that attending an Elderhostel is "the closest thing to being 19 again." This lifelong learning program allows you to go back to college for a modest price (about $275 for a one-week program). You'll meet and spend time with many classmates. Most libraries have Elderhostel catalogues.

If you're a recent widower, you may want to think about a bereavement group. Consider this possibility—one widower helping another, perhaps by introducing him to his sister or some other widowed relative.

How about joining a local political or civic action group? Save a river or adopt a highway and get out to rub shoulders with your good neighbors.

Light on your feet? Join a dance class (or group) at your local community college, YMCA, or senior center. At the very least, you'll be getting good, heart-healthy benefits from the exercise.

If you're considering placing an ad in the personals section of a newspaper or magazine, you're on your own. I've heard good, bad, and indifferent stories about these often-fictionalized come-ons. To spare embarrassment and to ensure your safety, always meet any prospective friend from these ads in a public place.

A few additional words now about overcoming the fear of dating. Shakespeare said it well for all of us when he wrote, "Our doubts are traitors / And make us lose the good we oft might win / By fearing to attempt." The fear of being rejected, romantically and sexually, present major obstacles to venturing out and moving forward. I remember clearly the angst and trepidation I knew as a 40-plus widower, wanting to date, yet believing that it was unseemly of me, a widower with three children and prematurely gray hair, to pick up the telephone to invite a woman I barely knew to meet me for dinner. I would walk around the phone, talking to myself like some pimply teenager seeking to woo the homecoming queen.

Ultimately, I concluded that the fear of dating and being spurned was only surpassed by the terrible, lonely feeling of sitting home alone night after night.

In the final analysis, you must think this way: "If I am determined to turn my life around and leave my loneliness behind, I must accept that some risk accompanies my challenge."

# CHAPTER TWENTY FOUR

# Reunions:

## BIG BUSINESS–AND YOUR BUSINESS, TOO

*"There is no hope of joy
except in human relations."*

—Saint-Exupéry

Quite simply, reunions are big business—and this big business continues to grow. These are the facts: presently some 30 million Americans, representing an estimated 14 percent of the population, come together each year in some form of a reunion.

Edith Wagner, editor of *Reunions*, a quarterly magazine published out of Milwaukee, explains that family reunions are the most numerous, but high school and college reunions are close behind with military reunions "a growth item, including a new and unanticipated spurt in Vietnam reunions."

I report this because it may be in your interest to participate in reunions. They are a way to make "new" friends with old pal and gal friends and you should not miss out on the nostalgia. It can be a boon and a tonic in hard times. As much as I dislike the word, reunions can bring *closure* to events that linger or even haunt you. And they give you a chance to fill out your score card, to see how well your life has gone and make a positive resolution for the future.

What follows are vignettes from reunions I've attended or written about. I want to spark your interest, set out a warning sign or two, and put you in the proper mood. Come on along.

On a rainy night that was perfect for amphibians, we came together in a rented hall for the impossible task of reliving the last half century. Yet none of the hardships seemed to matter as the Westwood (NJ) High School Class of 1946 staged its 50th anniversary reunion. The long room, decorated with crepe paper and flowers, was filled to overflowing with friendship, good cheer, and fond memories as gray-haired, laughing men and women reached back to recall only the good moments, buoyant times when, together, we groped toward adulthood.

As the recorded music began, featuring love songs from the 1940s and 1950s, Bob Vogler, a stalwart on the planning committee, swept to the dance floor with his wife, Winnie. In our school days, I recall young Vogler spoke only when spoken to, but here was a lean, vigorous man, obviously enjoying himself.

From the sidelines a woman classmate called out, "Hey Bobby, if I'd known you were going to turn out so good, I would have made a play for you myself!"

In fact, the entire night was marked with surprises, pleasant and otherwise. My wife Jan and I had traveled north from Georgia, while others came from California, Florida, Arkansas, Virginia, and Maryland. And one of us, Millicent (Millie) Liccardi, had come from a remote village in Brazil where she is a literacy teacher among the Indians of South America. At our crowded table of ten, the talk was free and easy. Yet one of our number, the victim of a stroke, sat silently except to comment "Golden years, phooey!"

That was the tough part of the assignment, seeing once care-free boys and girls of my youth showing the ravages of age. A particular pal, who suffers with emphysema, sat all night because he was too weak to table-hop or dance. Yet the majority of this group—there were 68 of us out of a class of 119—showed ourselves to be robust and socially upbeat.

Long after the event, I read through their thumbnail biographies and found one positive declamation after another. "I am blessed with a beautiful family. . . Married my high school sweet-heart, and they said it was just puppy love!. . . Things turned out much better than I thought they'd be. I feel blessed. . . My life has been a series of joys and heartaches, but intriguing and sur-prising, too. . . The Lord has blessed me with a wonderful wife of 42 years, [as well as] a zest for life, and energy and enthusiasm to make each day an experience of wonder."

Invariably, the five-and six-line items all carry the same sort of message: "The USS *Eisel,* the proudest fighting ship in the South Pacific, is staging a reunion next summer. Contact Frank Krawcyk, Chicago, Illinois."

As a columnist who sees dozens of similar notices in press releases, magazines, and senior newspapers, I was curious. Who are these resolute men with long memories? Why, after all these years, do they want to come together? For the majority of Americans, World War II is forgotten history. It's about a shadow time, a half century or more in the past. Here, though, is the unusual story behind one such reunion and why it has endured.

In the North Atlantic, more than fifty years ago, a German supply submarine (U-boat *490*) was pursued by an American destroyer-escort, the USS *Inch.* For hours, the two played a cat-and-mouse game. Ultimately, the USS *Inch* won. Battered by depth charges and no longer seaworthy, *U-490* surfaced and was further damaged by the *Inch*'s artillery guns until the U-boat commander was forced to scuttle his vessel. Frightened sailors, most of them teenage boys, leaped into the ocean, shouting "Long live Germany."

In the pre-dawn hours of June 12, 1944, the USS *Inch* and other attack ships sailed away, leaving the Germans to the mercy of the open sea. Two hours later, and for reasons unknown, the ships returned to rescue the now -weary, foundering submariners. One German sailor recalling the event, said, "It was a miracle come true. Hostility was put to rest, and humanity took over."

Today, warm hospitality has replaced hostility, because the ex-sailors of both navies gather on a fairly regular basis to swap lies, drink each other's beer and schnapps, and celebrate life after the war. William R. (Bill) Fehlinger of Egg Harbor Township, NJ, is the one who told me this story. He is chiefly responsible for the camaraderie.

"About 1984, we began to hold USS *Inch* reunions," he said. Since the battering of the German submarine had been the high-light of their wartime duty, much of the reunion talk was about the forty-one enemy sailors and six officers rescued from the waters north of the Azore Islands. Fehlinger, whose great-grandparents emigrated from Germany in 1863, began what he terms a low-key investigation.

"We were teenagers, they were teenagers," he says. "Maybe none of us understood what we were fighting for." Through a friend of a friend, Fehlinger found his way to Fiete Barghan who, like Bill, had been 17 when he enlisted and was assigned to *U-490*. The idea of a joint reunion was put forward and the Germans responded with enthusiasm.

"The USS *Inch* gave life back to us men," Fiete Barghan told Fehlinger in accepting an invitation to join the Americans. Later, he would explain "When we're together, it's a happy group, all of us intent on a good time."

I asked Fehlinger what the men do at the reunions. He seemed nonplused. "What do we do?" he repeated. "We eat, drink, talk. We all bring our albums, and go back over the photographs. We learn stuff we've forgotten for years."

It was a Lindeman family reunion that read like a Chinese menu. There we were, hard by the Atlantic Ocean in beguiling south Florida, eight adults and three grandchildren, all with crowded calendars and one desire—to be together, if only for a day or two.

As a 1990s family, with branches in suburban Atlanta, south Miami, and Oak Park, IL, we are forced to seize the moment whenever and wherever we are. This was one of those times when, through serendipity abetted by love, struggle, and dipping into emergency funds, we were all gathered at one place.

Leslie William Lindeman, the eldest, had telephoned. "You've got to come! It will be the first time we're all together since Natalie's christening." He referred to the baptism of his daughter, a command performance in suburban Chicago some eighteen months previous.

Seventy-two hours later, I was flanked on the battered family couch which anchors the living room of the Lindeman condo by three squirmy, ever-loving little girls. As the patriarch, it is my privilege to sit among these treasures named Melissa, Stephanie, and Natalie. At that moment, Natalie Adele was receiving the lion's share of attention because, hours before we all gathered, she had tumbled from a neighborhood swing and fractured the major bone in her lower right leg.

"Broken," she said, pointing at her soft cast. Later, this sweet-faced, tiny person would look down at her outsized brace and sternly direct, "Cast. Off!"

Between talking and eating and swimming, we made time for photographs. I remember someone shouting, "Everyone jump on Grandpa Bard, and we'll snap a picture!" In quick order, sons Les and Paul and their wives joined the cherubs and me on the couch. Next came daughter Janet and her running-coach/husband Greg Domantay. Then snap-click, the impromptu reunion was official, with eleven of twelve us accounted for. My wife Jan was busy with her work.

The two-bedroom condo at Lake Worth, which serves as our reunion headquarters, is an inheritance from my late mother, Martha Quitzau Lindeman. It is tradition that visitors—guests, family members, everyone—must record a message in the Lindeman log before they leave. This is our way of maintaining connections, links to one another, and our past. Son Les, keeper of the family history, is the most conscientious of the journal volunteers. It was he who, in 1986, put into words how collectively we felt at the graduation of Dr. Paul from the University of Miami medical school. His piece, which appeared on Mother's Day in the *Miami Herald*, took the form of a letter to his late mother.

"Our family is together again," he began. "It's been almost fifteen years since that night you left us, never to return. We have made it through the storm. Today is our day to celebrate. . . a time to honor Paul's accomplishment and our togetherness. How much he has grown. How much healing he will bring to people he doesn't even know. . . Although you are not here, we can see you in each others' faces. Thank you, Mom.

"If I could talk to the world on this day," he continued, "I would tell them to go find their mothers and hug them, then say those obvious things that somehow never get said."

Isn't that the way with family reunions? You get the chance with a look or gesture or even a touch to say "This is great. Our being together. I love you guys. Why don't we do it more often?"

Our times together, largely unplanned and too few, nonetheless make putting up with all the daily skirmishes, the struggles, and aggravations worthwhile. When I, the eldest by far, retire to bed and close the book on another day, I do so knowing that I leave behind in the living room love and laughter, the best of what we are—and that our group adds just a little bit of caring in a society beset and torn and ever in need of stable, intergenerational families.

# CHAPTER TWENTY FIVE

# God Made Bartenders

## SO MEN WOULD HAVE SOMEONE TO TALK TO

*"One loyal friend
is worth ten thousand relatives."*

—Euripides

W hy, I had long wondered, do older adults want to hunker down in hot, flat central Florida or off in the middle of Nevada, Texas, or southern California? Why do they build all those isolated gray communities around new golf courses?

The answer, quite simply, is companionship, kinship, and friendship.

Inside a cluttered, modest home I met and interviewed Dick Vance, a retired mid-westerner who introduced himself as "a rehabilitated cancer patient." Vance is also legally blind but he wanted me to understand at the outset that he was content and in control of his environment. He explained how he had been a cable television salesman and, judging by the electronic toys and tools which filled his ranch home, his vocation had become his hobby, if not his lifestyle. This voluble, recently remarried Floridian, 61 at the time, became euphoric when talking about his new friends.

"Your friends are everything," he began. "Look, about ten percent of any group our age have kids that dote on their parents. The other 90 percent have got to make another life, one built around their friends. Otherwise, you'll die of loneliness or boredom."

He told me how he loved playing golf, even though he couldn't see the pin from more than ten feet away. How then does he manage? "With friends," he said, matter-of-factly. "They call out to me, giving me sound signals. That's how I know where to hit it."

"I read somewhere," he said next, "that for older guys, one good friend is worth twelve grandchildren. I love my grandkids, but I believe this statement with all my heart."

I came away from that interview in Leesburg, FL, persuaded that I had witnessed a parable. A man who could not see normally had showed me why people who become your friends can make the retirement years worthwhile and productive. I learned through observation that Dick Vance is a happy soul, even though he must battle every day of his life. At the same time, I also felt that he represents an exception to the rule, because the melancholy truth is that most men, in middle age and beyond, know a lot of people, but have few—possibly too few—friends. As author Marc Feigen-Fasteau put it in *The Male Machine,* American men have carried "the practice of emotional restraint to the point of paralysis." This very paralysis oftentimes makes close friendships difficult, if not impossible.

Social scientists and writers of both sexes maintain that American men shy away from close friendships with other men. Oh, sure, they have pals and buddies, guys who are fishing partners, or golf opponents, someone to meet for a drink. But these are companions, people with whom they *do* something. They are not friends, not men they talk to, open up to, or to whom they show their vulnerable sides.

A journalist friend, Maurice (Mickey) Carroll, of New York City, once told me, "Men like to talk, but not necessarily with their close friends. That is why God invented bartenders."

It's different on the other side of the sexual divide, however. "Women tend to be more aware of themselves and their problems," according to author Eda LeShan. "They talk and talk and talk—and feelings flow freely."

When I was editor of *50 Plus* magazine in New York, I assigned writer Dan Cryer to explore male friendships and, specifically, to report on their difficulties. He wrote, "From the frontier days of old to the Marlboro Man of today, the [image of the] solitary hero has posed the most formidable challenge to friendship among men. . . [because] if friendship is to have any depth, it requires honesty and openness, warmth and empathy, a receptivity to others and a willingness to express feelings. These are precisely the qualities bred out of little boys as they grow to manhood."

Cryer concluded, "Macho toughness and self-reliance may keep the bad guys out of town, but it also keeps the good guys at arm's length. Granted, the boys at the bar provide plenty of camaraderie and carefree good times, but it is only in the arms of a woman that the American man may confess weakness and admit to uncertainty."

Some ten years after Cryer's article, the magazine, now known as *New Choices,* published a fine essay on the same subject by Laurence I. Barrett, a former writer and editor for *Time.* The piece was titled "Call Your Old Friends."

Barrett opened by explaining that he'd recently lost two dear longtime friends. He wrote that by "late middle age you're bruised by such bad news, but no longer astonished. You've already lost some contemporaries. And you've become all too familiar with the feelings of diminishment, anger, and anxiety. They were roughly your age (too young!), it was so sudden, it isn't fair. And, of course, who's next?"

Based on this experience, Barrett became determined to be a better friend to his friends, including the survivors from his old gang in the Bronx, NY, where he spent his boyhood. He concluded, "The old networks inevitably shrink, but they can endure for a long time if survivors make an effort."

That, to be sure, is the point! You simply must make that extra effort. Reach out to your friends. Today and every day, I want you to put one thing at the top of your "To Do" list that speaks to the fostering and/or reaffirming of your male friendships. It is in your best interest to follow this simple, common sense course of action, because almost every research study on the subject of friendships reaches the same conclusion: intimacy serves as a buffer to life's stresses.

In other words, having good friends is not only a good thing to do, it is a smart and healthful thing to do. Strong and constant friends are one key to longevity.

Finally, I offer you the comfort of this reaffirming thought from novelist Herbert Gold. "Yes, we are getting older. No, we're not alone. We have our friendships."

# A Good Guy Named Jack

Some male friendships can last a lifetime. I want to tell you about one such relationship.

We met in the 1960s because we both had sons the same age. They were Little Leaguers. His was a 12-year-old pitcher while mine was a catcher of 11. The boys liked one another, too. This was in the small town of Washington Township in northern New Jersey, but it could have been Anywhere, USA.

Jack genuinely loved my boy Les and I would have wrestled an alligator for his Tom. In what may have been the sanest move we ever made as fathers, we made an agreement about our sons. Since we both wanted our own number one progeny to be the best, we agreed that neither father would coach his own son. During a game, we couldn't even talk to our own sons. Meanwhile, we showed inordinate patience, relatively speaking, with every other father's son who played for us.

On one of the most memorable nights of my life as a parent, our team won the town championship for the 9–12 year olds. After the last out, all the sweaty, jubilant kids, along with a number of fathers and mothers, returned to our home for a backyard celebration. In a quiet ceremony, several of the older boys presented sterling silver mugs to Jack and me. Mine stands close by as

I write this. Its one-line inscription reads "Champs, 1969."

In a handful of baseball seasons, Jack Clarkson and I grew close while nurturing fifteen kids who had little in common when they had first met. Several, for sure, showed little baseball talent at the outset. But Jack and I held more practices and meetings than did the other teams. We joked around and worked with each boy, trying to tap his potential. We put in the time, willingly, because we enjoyed the experience and, without being particularly conscious about it, Jack and I bonded.

Being a journalism gypsy, I moved on to Chicago and then Miami, back to New York and finally suburban Atlanta. I lost touch with Jack, his wife Joan, and their four children. However, I got a lovely surprise in the mail one day when a letter arrived signed by Joan. She reported the family was all well, their children married with children of their own. Tommy, our ace pitcher, is an entrepreneur, marketing and selling *Field & Stream* wristwatches.

"Jack works for Tom as a repair person," Joan explained. "How is that for a career change? From printer to little old watchmaker. . . The entire family was together this past Christmas. I had shirts sent down from Clarkson University in upstate New York. We took pictures. . . ."

After I read the letter two or three times, I reached for the telephone. Jack's voice was a tonic and we picked up where we left off some thirty years before. He laughed often, dredging up twice-told tales and avoiding any mention of negative or troublesome news. We spent twenty minutes catching up and then I promised to visit Jack and his family, very soon.

Some older men can become quite capable of strong, enduring friendships, especially when they acknowledge that being genuine, being open, even vulnerable, are the keys to a good relationship.

Great to hear from you, Jack. ◆

# How Good a Friend Are You?

There's a maxim that teaches "You have to be a good friend to have a good friend." Take this simple test to see how well you score in the friendship category:

Do you have a pal on whom you can rely to help you with some yard work or to drive you to the airport?
Yes_____No _____

Do you belong to a church or temple, and are you friends with any of the male congregation members?
Yes____No____

Have you watched a sporting event on television, or attended one with other men during the past three months?
Yes_____No_____

Do you play cards or have a "night out with the boys" on a regular basis?
Yes____No____

During a medical emergency, is there a man-friend you would quickly turn to?
Yes____No____

Do you have a male friend to whom you would lend money, no questions asked?
Yes____No____

Do you take part in any of the following sports: bowling, golf, tennis, softball, fishing, swimming, boating?
Yes____No____

Have you attended a high school or college class reunion in the past five years?
Yes____No____

If you are a father to sons, are you able to depend upon them as "steady friends?"
Yes____No____

Have you gone on a day trip with one or more male friends in the last year?
Yes____No____

Give yourself one point for every "Yes" answer. If you scored 7–10 points, you're a swell pal to your friends. If your score was 5–7, you're a good friend. If you recorded 0–5 points, you need to get on the phone and call your friends. They're waiting to hear from you. ◆

# CHAPTER TWENTY SIX

# Old Fires,

## NEW SPARKS

*"The heart has its reasons
of which reason knows nothing."*

—Blaise Pascal

Heads turn ever so slightly when we enter a restaurant or other public place. My wife, who is blessed with what women commonly call good skin, is 26 years younger than I am and looks it. I, on the other hand, hold a Medicare card and have no difficulty convincing supermarket checkers and movie cashiers that I qualify for the senior discount.

To some, we might appear as father-and-daughter. Yet we've been married many years and I'm pleased to report that despite our considerable age disparity, the marriage is successful by all measures. The truth is, we both were single and unattached when we met by serendipity. Looking back, I can only believe it was magic. I'm fond of saying, "It was meant to be."

I had traveled to Atlanta to deliver a luncheon talk to the local chapter of Women In Communications and Janice Elaine Still, public relations person, was to introduce me. She held up my career resume and told our audience, "It says here that Mr. Lindeman jumps rope *good*. If his talk is no good, we'll just ask him to jump rope for us."

Afterward, Jan Still said, "I hope you didn't mind my making fun of you."

"It's been a long time since a woman made me laugh at myself," I remember saying. Later that night, emboldened, I telephoned this much younger woman and asked her out for a drink. We quickly, impetuously, fell in love and had a heady weekend courtship that continued for seven months. I sent Jan pre-paid airline tickets to come to New York where I then lived, or I would travel to suburban Atlanta to be with Jan. We enjoyed Broadway shows, movies, and concerts. We ate dinner out in both cities. We walked and talked and, from the outset, we laughed a lot.

"This romance," I said to Jan, "is going to last as long as my credit cards hold out."

Our ages mattered little then, and when I discovered—to my shock—that Jan Still was actually my junior by twenty-six years, that she and my eldest adult child were contemporaries, it was too late. I was in love. I was a widower, and a divorced husband as well, who was willing to roll the dice to take this big gamble. Sitting at a bar in a small Italian restaurant in Guttenberg, NJ, I suddenly threw out some bogus bachelor's line about how we would live "after we get married." She smiled, but didn't shoot me down. To myself I said, "It's going to work. I'll make it work!"

Later, walking a south Florida beach with my two mature sons, I told them of my plans and obliquely asked their blessing. Les, the eldest of my three children, said "Hey, you're the marriage expert in the family. You've had one great one, and one lousy one. What more do you need to know?"

To some readers this is certain to sound like so much twaddle and rationalization, but I believe at some level that I needed to remarry and wanted, at all costs, to enter a union where the wife would not die before me. I had been inside that hell on earth once and knew that no man should ever go through that experience *twice.*

On December 19, 1982, Jan and I were married in my hometown church in Westwood, NJ. My best friend, the late Leon J. Leslie, and his wife Nancy Hill Leslie, stood up for us. Other than the minister, no one else was present at that Sunday afternoon service in Zion Lutheran Church. Nonetheless, the minister loudly recited the words of the solemn ritual and his voice echoed throughout the high-ceilinged brick and stone building. Unable to control her swirl of emotions, Jan began to cry softly. I was moved by this sudden turn and nervously laughed out loud as I held and comforted my beautiful bride.

These days, there's talk about more older dudes marrying younger women. Here, though, are the facts: according to figures at the National Center for Health Statistics, some 10.2 percent of American males who married twenty years ago chose women 10 or more years younger than themselves. By 1983, that percentage had risen to 12.4. It has remained close to that figure ever since. But age-skewed alliances tend to make news, to draw attention and, yes, turn heads. To many these marriages are, in a word, outrageous.

Tabloid headlines might lead you to believe there are many more older male/younger female marriages than is the case. Celebrities Clint Eastwood, Warren Beatty, Tony Randall, Johnny Carson, Jack Nicholson, Anthony Quinn, and Ed McMahon are but a few of the senior men who sought out and married women junior to themselves. All of these examples plainly involve affluent, accomplished men who had been previously married. To a degree, they fit the societal definition of an older, lustful man-of-means chasing down, even buying, the affection of a younger squeeze.

Yet, it wasn't always this way. Sociologist Dr. Andrew Cherlin, of Johns Hopkins University, points out that "When we lived on farms and death rates were high, it was common for a widower to marry a young second wife, and then even have another child."

Now am I espousing, indeed advocating, that the intergenerational romance and marriage is the way to go? Do I mean to say that age differences play little or no part in the marital equation? No to both those appropriate questions. Moreover, I make no special plea in defense of my lifestyle. I do, however, ask for tolerance, even patience, when judging life-partners from different generations. Let me suggest that most often the accent in a senior/junior relationship is on the *relationship* and not on its age disparity. Son Les Lindeman looks at our marriage and says, "You're different in your tastes for music, reading, television, your approach to fashion and dress. You're different in outlooks toward money and you're at different stages of your careers. All of this is interesting, but differences can describe almost any relationship. Your bottom line is love. Age is an interesting component, but it's not the defining one."

The women readers of my column are less charitable when I write of our May-December marriage, and I understand their skepticism and scorn. A divorced professional woman in California, Heather E. Stiles, sent an impassioned critique beginning, "From absent fathers to delinquent dads, our society suffers from men whose sexual appetites define their generation. May-December marriages are another example."

Stiles, a baby boomer, argues that, "In the past, people grew old together and supported one another. We now find men dumping their wives for younger women in a sad attempt at a second youth. Or they're seeking mates dramatically younger than themselves when widowed. Most women find this amusing, sad, or painful."

I telephoned Heather Stiles and we had a good talk. Because she writes clearly and well, I invited her to contribute to my column again. This is how she closed out her concerned letter to me. "Bard, your personal story—about you and wife Jan—is a sweet one. But I wonder about it played out thousands of times around the country. And I wonder about myself and my friends, all vibrant people. To a newly single adult, what do you say? What can you say to these good women? Good luck?"

When heads turn toward Jan and me, I'm certain that a percentage of the onlookers—the senior women, at least—hold similar feelings. It is a price that all older men in relationships with younger women must pay. I accept that, just as I recognize that I cannot assuage the feelings and frustrations of the people who resent me. The fact remains, however, I am pleased and proud of my marriage. I also know that I'm not the only one who believes as I do. My friend and contemporary Edwin Kiester, Jr., is eleven years older than his second wife Sally. His close friend, whom we'll call George, 72, is twenty years senior to his second wife Sarah. You have only to meet these West Coast couples to learn through observation that their unity plainly rests on something more solid and lasting than immature leering and/or licentiousness.

Dr. Alex Comfort, the English-born author of *The Joy of Sex,* wrote, "Old people are therefore either loving people or tragic people who have outlived the quality of engagement. This is why compulsory exclusion and the impoverishment of daily experience which we often impose on the old are so profoundly damaging to them."

In other words, given the opportunity to love, to discover and further explore love, we should charge ahead. For in the words of author Eileen Simpson, writing in *Late Love: A Celebration of Marriage After Fifty,* "Late love is existential love. It reflects a poignant awareness that all life is transient, that existence is brief, that our days are numbered. Life becomes more precious because it is fleeting."

# CHAPTER TWENTY SEVEN

# Grandparenting,

## LIFE'S BONUS

*"Kids don't see wrinkles in their grandparents."*

—Dr. Arthur Kornhaber, author and president
of the Foundation for Grandparenting

C olor them small and smart and, just when you reach out to hold them, they turn wiggly. Yes, these are our grandchildren, and bless them, they've turned life around for all of us in the great Gray Legion, and taken the verb "love" to another level.

Grandparents, of course, are the mortar that holds multi-generational families together. They are teachers, nurturers, counselors, world-class listeners, and role models. With their lined faces and white hair, they speak of enduring and surviving. "If all of life's lessons were in books," says author and grandmother Lois Wyse, "there would be no need for grandmothers."

Child psychologist Eda LeShan recalls that her grandmother "never seemed to tire of talking to me. I remember her as the most comfortable person I ever knew. She always could make me feel safe, happy, and *loved*."

Love, then, is the greatest gift you can give your grandchild. I'm speaking now of unconditional love that says, again and again, "I love you, Melissa, Stephanie and Natalie Lindeman. . . I love you no matter what. You are MY grandchildren—and that, to me, is enough."

I remember with remarkable clarity the arrival of my first grandchild. From the first news that a baby was on its way, I had wanted to be there—on the spot—for the birth. Paul Lindeman was a medical resident in Jacksonville, FL, when his pregnant wife became a patient in the same hospital where her husband worked an interminable number of hours. I traveled from New York, did business in Orlando, then shuttled to Jacksonville. I missed the birth by two hours, arriving in the room just as Suzy Lindeman was nursing Melissa Adele for the first time. It remains a defining moment in my life.

That night, my proud son and I had a good dinner and excellent cigars. Afterward, we walked on the beach and under a pitch black sky, we talked for hours. Our world then was just about perfect.

Of course, I am not alone in my feeling that grandparenting is both a privilege and a life bonus. One of my readers, Kathy Mastrorocco, of Derry, PA, wrote to me explaining what her first grandchild meant to her. "People tell me that when someone asks about my grandchild, an immediate, wide smile appears on my face. After raising four sons and a daughter, I have had my share of smiles and joy. However, nothing prepared me for the life I have led since September 1, 1994, when, as dawn appeared, so also did my grandson, Michael."

Mastrorocco calls her grandson "my tonic for living. I never tire of looking at him. When he falls asleep in my arms, even the numbness, that pins and needles feeling, does not matter because he is so precious."

Over the fifteen-year course of writing my column, I have

received a good number of well written, heartfelt letters heaping extravagant praise upon grandchildren. One year, I finally got smart and announced I was sponsoring a contest, urging grandparents to send me their favorite story about a grandchild or grandchildren. The big reward—a $25 United States savings bond, and publication in their local newspaper.

That first year, I received fifty or so letters. The next year, there were four times as many letters, with thirty or more of them funny, clever, insightful, and touching. The majority, as you might suspect, were from grandmothers, but the second-year winner was proud grandpa Jack Jacobson, 77, of Tucson, AZ.

He set his story up by first explaining that for thirty years he and five friends, all of whom work in the entertainment industry, have regularly met for coffee. One of the highlights at these gab-fests is always "grandkid stories." Jacobson's narrative begins during a car ride with his "kind, intelligent, thoughtful, fun-to-be-with grandson, Brent Jacobson." This trip was different because, in grandpa Jack's words, "The little guy sat quietly in his seat, hands clasped in his lap. Usually, he is singing, laughing and joking."

"Brent, you okay?" asked the concerned grandparent. Then, after a nod yes, and a pause, the child said, "Grandpa Jack, what did you do before you had me when the guys [your friends] told grandkid stories?"

Grandpa Jack answered, "Well, I sat and listened and prayed that one day I'd have a wonderful grandson just like you so I then would have grandkid stories to tell."

Pleased with that answer, Jack Jacobson grinned, and then turned to monitor his grandson's reaction. The boy sat quietly, still in deep thought. "You know, Grandpa Jack," he said next, "when I was growing in Mama's belly, I prayed that I would have a wonderful grandpa, just like you."

Again, he was silent before adding: "And. . . I got him."

Jack Jacobson writes, "I had to slow the car down just then, for suddenly it became very difficult for me to see. . . ."

To be a card-carrying member in good standing of our Outrageous Older Men's Society, you should be a doting grandpa. Jacobson recognizes this. So does my friend Les Hanscom who grew up in a rural Maine town but now lives in New York City. This retired newsman wrote about the role of grandfather.

"When I was growing up, I was able to make myself a nuisance to my grandparents on a daily basis. I have a very warm memory of them and they are a part of what I am. As I face toward the time left, it consoles me to understand that I am only a blink. . . that the chain was a long one before it produced me as an ornament, and that I can hope it will be longer yet through the 6-year-old who is now forming his sense of the world by means of the cartoon channel on television. . . I wish I could meddle more [in his life] in a grandfather's way as that formation process goes forward. I fully trust his parents to guide it the right way, but my own growing up makes me feel that grandparents have special authority by virtue of their antiquity."

Psychiatrist Arthur Kornhaber of Santa Fe, NM, has devoted much of his career to studying the relationship between the generations. He calls the bond joining grandparent to grandchild "the vital connection." He further believes that the happiness created when the pair is together "contributes to the health and well-being of both generations."

This brings me to a juncture where I must censure those grandparents who fall down on their responsibilities. They're out there, hiding behind a mask of selfishness or disinterest. Not long ago, I received an unsigned letter from a mother who was anguished because her in-laws are guilty of what she considers emotional neglect. The woman wrote, "Grandchildren grow up so fast, don't they? I am fortunate my parents shower our kids (ages 11 and 14) with love and attention, and that is a precious sight for us to witness. On the other hand, my husband's parents don't see our kids. The children play Little League, yet the paternal grandparents don't even come to a game. I know they love their only grandchildren, yet it's beyond my understanding how they can just, well, ignore them!"

I find myself agreeing with this bewildered mother. I cannot fathom grandparents who fall short on their emotional and time commitments to their flesh and blood, their grandchildren. Strengthening the bond or contract between the generations is one sound, rational reason to lead a long and outrageous life. As the late Maggie Kuhn reminded us, "Our job is to secure the future for the young."

Lastly, these few words of counsel to grandparents. Understand that grandchildren want you to show off your knowledge and experience, the natural byproducts of living long. This is all part of how grandkids grow to feel secure and comfortable alongside their affectionate, generous elders. Meantime, recognize that you cannot actually spoil a grandchild, at least not with love.

To the contrary, children blossom and mature in response to a grandparent's love.

# Ten Slightly Outrageous Ways to Spoil Your Grandchild

1. The world of children is ruled by visual stimuli. Make a video explaining to your grandchild the ten reasons you have for loving him or her. Introduce yourself as "Grandpa, the All-knowing, A Star for the Ages." Ham it up, big time. Wear an old derby and bib overalls as your costume.

2. Grandparents should be full of surprises. Why not host a pajama party for your grandchild and his or her two best friends? Have plenty of popcorn on hand.

3. On a day when it's raining cats and dogs, show up at your grandchild's house. Tell him or her it's a perfect day for learning about watercolors.

4. Spend an afternoon together at the library. Teach your grandchild that she never again will be alone so long as a good book is close by.

5. Treat your grandchildren to a major league (or minor league) baseball game. For many kids, the first such adventure becomes an unforgettable, bonding experience. This is one time when you can tell "In my day" stories. You have free license to talk about Willie Mays, Joe Dimaggio, Jackie Robinson, Brooks Robinson, and others whom you saw make baseball history. If you

have old-time autographs to show off, so much the better.

6. If you're lucky enough to live close by your grandchildren, try to squeeze in as many dance recitals, class plays, Girl Scout jamborees, and Little League games as you can. Grandparents make wonderful, uncritical cheerleaders.

7. A grandchild must learn about money. Give yours a small allowance, then help her open a savings account, with parental approval, of course. Walk her into the bank as though you both sit on the board of directors. From that moment on, refer to the institution as her bank.

8. It's a commandment: honor the budding skills and talents of each grandchild. Frame the first painting, poem, or essay presented to you and display it in a favorite part of the house.

9. Swimming is among the best of exercises and once learned, you can swim for a lifetime. Treat your grandchild to swim lessons—only a few are needed—and then show up in a bathing suit yourself to enthusiastically applaud each new water accomplishment. Let the water be your shared environment. A pool or the ocean is a natural setting for laughter, fun, splashing, teasing, sharing tricks, and exercise.

During my years as a widower, I took my daughter Janet for swimming lessons every Monday night. I swam laps while she was learning to be comfortable in the water with her instructor. For us, this was our night out together. Her two brothers, meanwhile, were at home doing school work. As a collegian, Janet swam four years on the Gettysburg (PA) College women's varsity and today is an amateur triathlete. Her best event, by far, is swimming.

10. Most grandkids have to be taught to eat vegetables. When your grandson balks at eating Brussels sprouts or broccoli, you eat them. Explain then that football linebackers, firemen, school teachers, doctors, and even lawyers must eat their vegetables, especially ones colored green, orange, and yellow. Follow up this meaningful experience with a book, pamphlet, or magazine article. One day your grandchildren will thank you, but not anytime soon.

If you're interested in learning more about grandparenting, you may want to be in touch with the **Foundation for Grandparenting**, c/o Arthur and Carol Kornhaber, 53 Principe de Paz, Santa Fe, NM 87505. ◆

# YOUR
# *Outrageous*
# SPIRIT

# CHAPTER TWENTY EIGHT

# Absent Friends:

## DEALING WITH HURT, LOSS, GRIEF

*"Can I see another's woe, and not be in sorrow, too?*
*Can I see another's grief, and not seek for kind relief?"*

—William Blake

How do we survivors, members of the legion of Successful Agers, cope with the sadnesses which inevitably find us as we move from one year to the next? This question or one much like it found its way into my professional mail bag not long ago. I began my answer something like this:

Your inquiry calls for the wisdom of Solomon, the caring qualities of Mother Teresa, and the humility of Dr. Albert Schweitzer. Nonetheless, I'll take a crack at answering how you handle the depression you now face following the recent death of several lifelong friends. Permit me to speak to you out of my own experience, for in my lifetime I have buried or helped bury a father and mother, two paternal grandparents, a beloved aunt, a father-in-law, and a handful of other relatives as well as a number of male friends. My oldest, dearest friend, Leon J. Leslie, died of cancer not long ago. He was as close to me as any family member and his loss, I know, will be with me always.

Oftentimes, I cannot remember where I read something, or whether I made my car payment. Yet I can easily recall most of the funerals I've attended, in particular those moments when I've stood by the bier, silently talking to the lifeless form before me.

But the most difficult loss I've ever faced was the tragic, wrenching, numbing experience of the death of my first wife. I recall those early days of grief and shock as though they were last week. The three children and I were all desperate and confused, when a longtime friend, novelist and freelance writer W.C. (Bill) Heinz, literally came to our rescue. Immediately following the funeral services—one in suburban Chicago where we lived and a second in New Jersey, which we considered "home"—Bill Heinz drove us to his mountain home outside Dorset, VT. Here we spent four or five days in isolation and solitude, ebbing and flowing with no schedule and, blessedly, no responsibilities. We were able to take long walks in the woods and swim in the chilly waters of a pond on the Heinz property.

I still cherish the memory of the two youngest children, irre-pressible, effervescent Paul, and his then shadow-worshipper Janet contentedly playing at the water's edge, discovering tadpoles and water bugs. They screamed in delight at each sighting. And why not? These two were just being children again, and in their nat-ural behavior I saw hope for us, hope for renewed life as a family.

Now I call up this time because it exemplifies my wish for everyone who hurts following a loss. It is important to find a quiet spot to regroup, a comforting place apart to begin the grieving process away from well-meaning yet invading eyes. It's important, too, to be away from people with their well-inten-tioned, unsettling questions and comments.

Our Vermont retreat was perfect for our purposes. We had only the rugged Green Mountains for outdoor companions, and there was no one close by to care if we made discomforting sounds, such as sobs or guttural curses while tears coursed down sad, swollen faces. Shakespeare, of course, was correct—time, much time, is balm for psychic wounds.

We Lindemans came down from our mountain retreat stronger and with renewed resolve to build our new lives, individually and as a family. Of course, we had help as we waged our campaigns. Here, then, are some of the outside influences which may support you in the healing process, a period that knows no timetable and cannot be predicted by a therapist or other medical doctor.

- Bereavement classes or courses are often available at churches, temples, YMCAs, senior centers, and community colleges. As a widower of 41, I chose not to go this route, calling instead upon my minister, the scholar and gentleman Reverend Dean Lueking. When I had asked about help for the children, Dean volunteered to be their counselor. Moreover, he was by my side from the first hours following Del Lindeman's death. My advice to hurting widowers, however, is to seek a bereavement group.

    Following a column I wrote on widowers, I received a long and thoughtful letter from Walter D. Fitzgerald. This New Jersey man wrote, "There are times when we can't stand alone. When we are sick, we see a doctor. When we are hurting, and fighting through grief, we badly need the support of others. Preferably, we need help from those who've been in the same position."

    I was impressed with Fitzgerald's letter and telephoned this widower. We spoke for an hour. During the conversation, I learned Fitzgerald is now a bereavement counselor. He also met his second wife through attendance at bereavement sessions. "I've seen that it's very hard for men to grieve," he told me. "From the time we're little, we're taught that strong men have a stiff upper lip—and don't ever cry."

- Widowers, and others who are hurting, need to learn that books can become their new friends. In this noisy era of visual overload there is therapy to be found inside a quiet room with an unread book to grace the hours in front of you. Most towns and all cities have fine libraries. As the son of a onetime librarian, I am prejudiced in favor of these institutions just waiting to enrich our lives. Visit yours, please. The section marked for bereavement and healing should afford you help.

- Volunteer service can take you down any number of fascinating roads and carry you toward better days. If you've read the chapter on volunteering, you already know that some adventurers join the Peace Corps, while many choose to sign up with the American Association of Retired Persons or Foster Grandparents. Still others find their private cause to which they commit time, energy, zeal—and feel better for it.

  When my longtime friend and soul-mate T. William (Bill) Hentz died shortly after he retired, his wife Carol established a scholarship fund in his name at our *alma mater,* Middlebury College in Vermont. Bill and Carol had met on campus and later built their retirement home overlooking this picturesque town. Well, Carol has been a demon, boosting this voluntary fund over the $332,000 mark in fewer than fifteen years, assuring that each year a minority student can attend Middlebury College a little more comfortably. I know that Carol's time as a widow has been made more meaningful and perhaps brightened as a result of her eminently worthwhile idea.

- Travel, whether it's to see the beauty of a Vermont fall, the ticky-tack of Florida, or the grandeur of the Swiss Alps, is recommended. The open road can be your route to escape, to see new faces and encounter new experiences. Once again, the idea is to gently, almost imperceptibly, turn a new page, chart a new course and move on—putting distance between you and your bad time.

- Grandkids—say the word and you can feel the softening of your facial muscles. Did you just grin? Proud and expansive grandparents continue to write my column, sending along stories about their precocious grandchildren. With the memory of these glowing notes in mind, I suggest that when you're ready, a therapeutic visit to these little people sounds like a good move.

- Pets are man's (and woman's) best friends, in part because they offer daily unconditional love and approbation. As the late Christopher Morely observed, "No one appreciates the very special genius of your conversation as a dog does." Not far from where I write this, my four-footed pal Nicky awaits my pleasure. When either Jan or I enter a room, Nick is there to wag his tail, ever ready for a walk, a run, a car ride, fun, whatever. But then if you've read "A Love Story" following Chapter Fifteen, you already know that I'm beyond the divide in my prejudices for pet therapy.

    The Purina Pets for People program works to foster animal adoptions by older adults. They offer a free brochure explaining the simple process. Write to Pets for People, NU World Marketing Ltd., PO Box 15791, Macoutah, IL 62224. Ask for "Pets for People: How to Find the Perfect Pet."

As I make these suggestions, I realize there is no way to immunize anyone from hurt, nor is there a way to make bereavement tolerable. When bad times fall on us, the pain must be endured and lived through. Each of us must find his own way through the rough patch. I can only hope this brief chapter is of some small help when it is your turn under the yoke of grief.

# CHAPTER TWENTY NINE

# Men without Women—

## NOT ALWAYS A PRETTY PICTURE

*"Aloneness is an activity.
Loneliness is a state of mind."*

—Louise Bernikow

One day, quite suddenly, you are alone. You didn't anticipate this. No one ever sat you down and said, "Your wife may die. She can die before you, despite those actuarial tables." No one bothered to remind you that in the United States, divorce is a given. It happens in upwards of 50 percent of all marriages—and few of us are immune.

I have been, quite suddenly, alone under both those circumstances. Neither is a walk in the park. However, as a result of considerable struggle and survival, I now consider myself a veteran on the negative subjects of loneliness and depression. Following the death of my first wife, and after a long healing process, I determined to write a primer on coping as a newly single adult. Pushing modesty aside, I think my advice is still sound.

If you're in the first months of being on your own, or even if you've been struggling to cope for a longer time, there are three essential things you should know to get on with your rehabilitation.

First, you are not the only one to carry this cross. An estimated one-fourth of all American households are occupied by just one person. Indeed, since 1960, the population of singles has tripled to more than 24 million and by the year 2000, an additional 7.4 million will have joined this gathering of men and women who are on their own.

Life for the newly single is a mixture of frustration, confusion, small successes, inevitable loneliness, and sadness punctuated by the exhilaration people feel when they are managing or coping.

Life, to be sure, is different. The challenges come hurtling toward you day after day. Sociologist and author Jane Seskin explains that "You can cry and feel sorry for yourself or you can say, 'This is the way it is' and make the best of your life."

The early days are the worst. I remember how it was after the death of my young wife. "The house is empty. The grandmothers and the aunts have all gone," I wrote for my magazine, *Today's Health*. "Les, Paul, and Janet are back in school. I have all day, every day, to myself. In the army, far from home in strange, spartan barracks, surrounded by alien faces and hostile noises and smells, I knew loneliness. Yet nothing in my life's experience has conditioned me for these first days and weeks alone, truly alone."

The actress Helen Hayes once said, "We all have two things in common when it comes to feeling lonely: we don't know how to talk about it, and we usually are a little bit ashamed."

Well, it's not worth feeling ashamed. It is worth talking about. Yes, loneliness is a universal, human condition, but it can be handled, thwarted, and over time, defeated.

Attitude will be the key to recovery in your life as a newly single person. Whether you're widowed, divorced, or have elected to remain unmarried, understand that the support for your single life is out there. It becomes your challenge to get back into the social mainstream and to find your way.

As a widower, I heard all the platitudes including "Life is for the living." What heartless, inane palaver, I thought at the time. Today, years later, I know this wisdom is true and worth repeating. To all those who live alone or struggle with loss, I have one message—be patient with your healing, yet remain resolute. Be hopeful, always, and learn to seize the good moments with your family and friends. Know, too, that life holds inexorably to its own pace and that none of us should ever voluntarily withdraw or accept the role of non-participant.

Given half a chance, the human spirit can and will regenerate.

To help you in your campaign, here are ten commonsense bits of advice I culled from my experience. Consider them as you craft your own style of coping.

1. Beware of bad advice. Listen only to trusted family members, longtime friends, or a professional counselor. If you're fortunate enough to have a widower for a friend, seek him out. Further, do nothing quickly or impetuously, such as selling your home or moving far away, in the hopes of outrunning your bad times.

   Soon after my wife died, well-meaning people came to me and asked, "What are you going to do with the kids?" Others suggested that I would want to sell our home, "to get away."

   I decided not to sell the house. It was, after all, our home and we were comfortable there. As for the children, they were my anchor, my grip on reality. They were the best reason I could find for getting up every morning. In those early, dark days I listened to my heart and instincts for survival. You should, too.

2. Build a support team. Start with old reliables, pals or family members you can call to talk with, ask along for a long walk. If you're a new widower, select a team captain and let him (or her) know when you're ready for visitors.

3. The healing of every widowed person or divorcée proceeds at a different pace. There is no calendar to announce when you are eager to talk, to socialize, to get away from routine. I remember times when people telephoned and I resented the intrusion. Other nights, I would stare at the phone and wonder, "Why doesn't someone call? Don't they know what I'm going through?"

   In fairness, how could they? I was at fault for not sending signals, cues that I needed companionship, kinship, kindness.

4. Alone or not, you've got to eat—and you must eat well and wisely. It is easy, freighted now with grief, to take the path of least resistance. Most men, even in good times, choose food that's easy to cook, or serve (cereal and bagels are favorites of mine), often neglecting what is nutritious.

   Eating properly begins with the will to do it, and ends with the feeling of pride and accomplishment that comes from doing something good for yourself. I am not comfortable in the role of pedant or scold, but I do feel I should tell you that the American Cancer Society estimates that at least 35 percent of all cancers are related to diet. The society's top four nutritional advisories for a long and healthy life are:

   Reduce all fatty foods. Start by eating less red meat and fried or processed foods.

Eat more fiber-rich foods.

Put more fresh fruits and vegetables in your diet.

Cut back on salt in your cooking, and eat food that is not high in sodium.

In order to follow these guidelines, you must read the labels on everything you buy. Be particularly vigilant about "hidden" sugars, fats, and salt.

And you've got to exercise. Study after study has shown that regular exercise is one of the best cures for depression.

It's no accident these are also ways to avoid obesity, high blood pressure, and coronary artery disease.

Being a little lazy about your meals, on occasion, is nothing to be worried about. But if you go from week to week indulging in self-neglect, you're telling yourself, "I am not worth any fuss or bother." That's not the attitude of a man determined to be a survivor.

5. Think of others and volunteer. By reaching out, you invite people to reach into your life. There are any number of quality organizations that need your time and talents. I personally am partial to the Meals-on-Wheels group and, because I once worked for their national organization in New York, the American Lung Association. In my mind, the association receives too little credit for its efforts, yet it continues to be among the most determined campaigners for clean air and a smokeless society.

6. Smile—you're a coping person. Remember, conversation takes two people and, here's the rub, both partners need to listen as well as talk. Incidentally, you'll be surprised how many chance conversations start when one person simply smiles. It's as good as a hello. In *How To Get Married Again,*

author Harriet Ryder said, "By smiling more often you are on your way to leaving your martyrdom behind. Smiling is a wonderfully warm habit that will make you and everyone else feel good."

7. Now's the time to search out your hidden talents. During an interview with journalist Walter Cronkite, I asked him what makes for a good retirement. He said, "I think happiness in older age and retirement is in direct relation to the diversity of interest. I think the serious problem is with that individual who has a single interest—in a shoe store, or whatever—and then retires from it and is completely lost."

Building upon that response, I urge you to find a neglected or hidden talent, some interest you had as a young man. Do you want to act? Join a local theater group. If you were a political science major forty-five years ago and never followed up on your cerebral love affair, why not join the "Silver-Haired Legislature"? Discover why your state budget doesn't balance, or why Medicaid is costing too much. Or, if you're out of patience with drunk drivers, open your telephone directory and call RID (Remove Intoxicated Drivers) or MADD (Mothers Against Drunk Drivers).

Author and businessman Ken Dychtwald, Ph.D., of Emeryville, CA, says that for too many people "The very prospect of aging imprisons them." There probably is no better way to break out of your bonds then to take a local college course—or join Elderhostel.

Elderhostel began in 1975 as a summer program for some 220 students and now provides educational opportunities for over 300,000 students age 55 years and older. It operates in more than 1,800 locations in the United States and Canada as well as in forty-five foreign countries. As a hosteler, you can sign up for a one, two, or three-week stay on a college campus of your choice and, for a relatively modest fee, take three college level courses. This fee includes a stay in a dorm room, cafeteria meals, and certain extracurricular activities. For information, write **Elderhostel**, 75 Federal Street, Boston, MA 02110-1941, or telephone (617) 426-7788. Courses are offered year-round at many sites.

8. Be a host and throw a dinner party. A divorced pal of mine lives alone in a fourth floor walkup in New York City's West Village neighborhood and is among the most contented people I know. He reads, attends plays, concerts and, on occasion, the opera. Not long ago he told me that he can't remember the last time he was lonely. Granted, he is well read, even cultured, and retired from *Newsday*, the Long Island newspaper he long served as book editor, columnist, and contributing writer. He also is a skilled chef who enjoys hosting small dinner parties for members of his fascinating array of friends and acquaintances. While he doesn't normally fuss over the meals he takes alone, he deliberately over prepares for parties. On the nights following these get-togethers, he continues to garnish and warm up his leftovers. "It's one of the reasons I like to throw a party," he said, laughing at his own foible. "I know that for the next week or so, I'm going to eat well."

My counsel is to do likewise. And if you're not a virtuoso in the kitchen, fix something simple. If you choose, practice the dish a couple of nights ahead. Remember, by entertaining, you are telling your world that you're ready for laughter, new experiences, companionship. Further, your stint as a host will most likely set off a chain reaction among the grateful guests who will return your invitation with ones of their own.

9. Are you ready for dating? There's no subject more enmeshed in emotions, confusion, and misconceptions than dating when you're newly single. I told my children shortly after their mother's death that I was not going to become a monk and had every intention of seeing other women—and I did. I also concluded, following a number of clumsy attempts, that the one thing harder than dating as a middle-aged widower was staying home night after night.

Now, what about sex? I offer this observation from sociologists Jan and Willard K. Kohn, authors of *The Widower.* "Probably the greatest help in coping with sexual frustration comes from the realization that most sane people don't expect widowed persons to quit being sexual at the death of their spouses."

I can assure you that you will hear ample advice with regard to sex, most of it, but not all, well-meaning. One woman, wife to a friend, insisted to me, "Remember, sex is solace." I think she was advising that I sleep around as a way to assuage my grief.

As with all decisions, you must proceed according to your personal timetable and code of behavior, with safe sex in mind, of course. However, when you achieve a strong identity and learn to value yourself apart from any past relationship, you'll become more confident and attractive as a date. Moreover, you'll feel far better about those unavoidable times when you find yourself alone.

10. Understand that grief is not an orderly process and no two people endure this tricky life passage according to the same timetable. Widows often hear, "Why doesn't she snap out of it? It's been a year since Paul died." As for widowers, we're not supposed to cry. Crying, say these uninformed

observers, is a sign of weakness, indicative of emotional upset or problems.

Philosopher Benjamin Blech once asked, "Can we possibly expect someone to cope with a loss he [or she] has not yet been forced to acknowledge? It is the tragedy of our times that we consider nature's way of healing a weakness, even as we continue to confuse emotion with immaturity. When I see models of self-control, I weep for them."

Yes, cry—cry for yourself as a man who has lost his woman, and encourage your friends and relatives to release their own feelings. Also, be patient with your grief. Be deliberate, conservative, and cautious in all new undertakings. Know, too, that you will go through a series of stages: grief, loneliness, guilt, anger and, above all, a sense of unreality.

As a new widower, I sometimes believed that I heard my wife in another room, and several times on crowded streets I sensed that I'd caught sight of her, just up ahead. I also imagined that I heard her talking to me, suggesting that I make this or that decision, and lovingly urging that I get on with my life. All of these things, I later discovered from my reading on grief, are common and natural.

It takes at least a full year to maneuver through the full range of emotions that surround grief. Let me assure you that in time you will sleep restfully though the night, your food will taste good again, you'll laugh and sing and enjoy music and movies and the company of friends. You will take delight in your children and grandchildren, becoming proud beyond all reason because they are growing, prospering, and caring of you and your contentment.

You will heal. You will eventually throw off your lassitude and work through your sorrow and anger. We have but one choice:

to make this life as good as we know how for ourselves and our heirs.

Finally, you must get to know and like your new self. You must become comfortable in your new lifestyle and find things about it to enjoy. As a coping person, you'll go on to meet people who genuinely want to share your life and make it even fuller, richer, more meaningful.

May that happen for you, and soon.

# CHAPTER THIRTY

# Presenting an All-Outrageous Team—

## WHO WOULD YOU CHOOSE?

*"We do not count a man's years until he has nothing else to count."*

—Ralph Waldo Emerson

There's a time-honored tradition that celebrates performance, achievement, and testosterone—the selection of the "All-America" teams grandly announced toward the end of each football season.

In another era, I was selected to the honorable mention roster of an All–New England team, as chosen by a Boston newspaper. I was probably an automatic choice, since I had played four seasons for Middlebury College and was the senior captain. No matter, I clipped the article and pasted it in a scrapbook, a collection of yellowing clippings my mother sheltered for years.

Your task now is to name your own All-Outrageous eleven, made up of stalwarts, role models, unquestioned contributors to society. Undoubtedly, your candidates will exemplify the precept that the formula for successful aging is an active engagement with life. They will be men on the front lines, meeting new challenges, helping others, or entertaining, serving, speaking out for causes. Let's honor them as outrageous pioneers of aging.

This is my All-Outrageous eleven. Every one of them is at least 55 years old.

1. Former President Jimmy Carter (1977-81) is far more popular today than when he was in the White House. His efforts on behalf of the homeless are one reason. His work for Habitat for Humanity reveals this Georgian's commitment to peoples of all races, creeds, politics. While some think of Carter as a world meddler, the fact remains he will travel anywhere (Haiti, East Africa, the Near East), ignoring risks to his health and safety, to engender peace and good works. And one day he may be awarded the Nobel Peace Prize. In his hometown of Plains, it's a special occasion when this onetime president returns to teach Sunday school. Tourists line up for early seats. Would that our nation produced more men and women who chose to walk in the righteous path so familiar to this white-haired man called by a boy's name.

2. Next up is C. Everett Koop, M.D., the blunt spokesperson on behalf of good health practices. He oftentimes is referred to as "America's doctor," and for good reason. While serving as Surgeon General of the United States, he directed an effective and persistent campaign against the national addiction to cigarette smoking. His work is responsible in large part for today's smoke free laws and a nationwide change in attitudes toward smoking. This onetime prac-

ticing pediatrician now speaks up in behalf of other responsible measures, such as regular exercise and a prudent diet. He has branded obesity our current "Public Enemy Number One." Long past the retirement age, this trusted medical missionary finds no reason to slow his pace or retreat into the background.

3. Louis "Studs" Terkel is a Pulitzer Prize–winning author *(The Good War),* oral historian, and in the words of *The New York Times,* "a wise and watchful chronicler of life and hard times in the United States." Born in New York City, but a Chicagoan since age 8, Terkel is as much a part of his hometown as that basketball team with all the trophies. Famous as an interviewer, with an unusual talent for listening—he was a radio host for forty-five years—Terkel has 9,000 hours of taped conversations, all of which he's giving to the Chicago Historical Society. (It's of small consequence, but two of those hours are interviews with me. I appeared once as an author, and a second time as the "fired" editor of *Today's Health* magazine.)

   Terkel's books *(Division Street, Hard Times, Working, American Century),* are collages of people, most of them unknown, the so-called little people who make our cities run, all speaking about their lives and their aspirations.

4. Charles M. Schultz is the genius behind the comic strip *Peanuts* and its gang of underachievers. Schultz, in my view, is our modern day Mark Twain, reminding us again and again of the merits of laughter and fun.

   Lessons from the Schultz lexicon:

   "Maybe the real secret to not getting old is not to grow up. I'm not a complete grown-up, really."

   "People ask me if there's any message, or theme, to

*Peanuts*. I suppose it might be that Charlie Brown, in spite of always losing, never gives up."

"Older people can become boring very easily. The way to prevent that, I suppose, is by maintaining an interest in others and forgetting about yourself."

Lastly, few realize it, but Schultz built an ice arena across from his California home so he and others (the arena is open to the public), could skate and, in his case, indulge a passion for ice hockey—as a player, no less!

5. My fifth choice is master musician Tony Bennett, who left his professional heart in San Francisco, as well as Chicago, Miami, St. Louis, New York, or wherever he roams, to deliver his timeless vocal renditions. I also include Tony Bennett because of his versatility. His painting is excellent. And I give him high marks for his work as an intergenerational music man. His ballads appeal to fans of all ages.

6. Reverend Billy Graham belongs in the "All-Outrageous" starting lineup for his lifetime of preaching, of carrying the gospel he knows well to the far corners of the earth, and for helping to shine light upon darkness and ignorance. In recent years, Parkinson's disease has forced this gentle, uncommon man to curtail his customarily frenetic schedule, but his courage and persistence still make their mark. Graham has been an American original as well a moral man for a most immoral time.

7. Henry Aaron, known widely as Hammerin' Hank, came out of Alabama poverty and had to abide and overcome pervasive racial prejudice. He nonetheless broke Babe Ruth's all-time home run record (714) and became a national sports hero, an authentic Hall of Fame athlete. When he

was finished with baseball, Aaron had 755 career home runs, a record that may stand for all time. Working today in the Ted Turner business empire, Aaron deserves more from major league baseball. He has earned the right to serve as an ambassador of his sport. In an era when too many professional athletes are boorish, overpaid, woefully inarticulate, and egocentric, Aaron represents dignity and character.

8. Representing the theater is tall, dignified Morgan Freeman, a man whom film critic Pauline Kael called "one of America's greatest actors." Freeman was already 50 when he was "discovered" in a film called *Street Smart* in which he played a pimp. Thereafter, he was acclaimed for his portrayal of the ever patient and kindhearted chauffeur in *Driving Miss Daisy* opposite the exquisite Jessica Tandy, and for his acting in Steven Spielberg's drama about the horrors of slavery, *Amistad.* A three-time nominee for an Academy Award and the recipient of an honorary degree from Rhodes College in Oxford, England, Freeman carries none of the trappings or the attitude of a celebrity. He lives in central Mississippi, explaining, "My home is a place where I just live, raise my horses, and tend to my gardens." A passionate sailor and lover of the open seas, he dreams of sailing around the world.

9. Arnold Palmer is referred to by sports writers as "the Legend from Latrobe," referring to his Pennsylvania hometown. Following surgery for prostate cancer, Palmer, white-haired and carrying extra pounds at his midsection, quickly returned to tournament golf, declaring, "I still love to play and still love the competition." To other men his age who feel sorry for themselves, Arnie is an inspiration. He persists in leading the active life, most of it in the public arena and

as commander-in-chief of Arnie's Army of fans. He's also a television pitchman for hearing aids, tractors, and whatnot. Millions of all ages continue to rally behind this millionaire with the unaffected ways.

10. Ted Turner may be the most outrageous man of money this nation has ever produced, and we're all better for that fact. He once said, "I think it would be tragic to just be remembered for making a lot of money. Having a huge amount of wealth—I liken it to eating popcorn. It fills you up, but it's not satisfying. If you have a strong philanthropic component in your life—I mean, you never see someone who lives a life of service commit suicide."

In 1997, Turner pledged to give the United Nations one billion dollars. Not bad for a man known as the Mouth of the South, an innovator who created a television news network with worldwide ramifications.

11. Joseph Vincent Paterno has been head football coach at Pennsylvania State University for more than thirty years. In fact, the players he first tutored as an assistant coach are drawing Social Security today. But there is no rocking chair in Joe's immediate future. "He's not aging. He just keeps going," says one of his Nittany Lion defensive linemen. "Best of all, he still gets excited about every new team."

This enthusiastic man has guided Penn State to two national championships and a Big Ten Conference championship. Paterno-coached teams have played in twenty-eight bowl games. All this, however, is only about football. Joe Paterno, the man and mentor, is more than football scores. He makes sure his players understand discipline. They behave on and off the field, they study, they graduate, and go on to good jobs. "The phrase student-athlete is not an oxymoron at Penn State," a newspaper once said.

Afterwards, the players come back to thank and hug "the old man." This intergenerational example of genuine teamwork strikes me as downright outrageous.

In addition, Joe and his wife Sue have given $3.5 million to Penn State to endow faculty positions, scholarships, and to support two building projects. This is no ordinary coach.

# These Men Deserve Recognition, Too

I know what you're thinking—Ted Turner, Arnold Palmer, Jimmy Carter, all millionaires. What do you have in common with these men, you ask. And I wish Lindeman would write about the regular guys who are outrageous like my next-door neighbor or my brother-in-law.

I hear you—you're talking straight. So let me introduce you to the outrageous older men who live right next door.

Merwyn Bagan is a neurosurgeon who retired from private practice to pursue a second career when he was nearing 60. Shortly thereafter, he began commuting from his home in Concord, NH, to Boston University in pursuit of a master's degree in public health administration. When he finished, he decided to give something back to the world for all the gifts he had enjoyed. So he and his wife Carol moved to Katmandu, Nepal, to teach Nepali doctors the art and skills of surgery, particularly brain surgery.

When his daughter Karin nominated him in response to one of my columns, she wrote, "He's been working without pay and staying in a two-story Nepali household that is situated along a mud road. My father and mother live without refrigeration or potable water. They are staying at least another year until the neurosurgery unit has a Nepali leader and becomes a self-sustaining unit."

Elden "Ike" Eichorn lived for many years in Elmore, MN, but now considers himself a citizen of the world. Ike is now in his eighth decade. He grew up on an Iowa farm without electricity, telephone, or running water. One of eleven children, he was expected to grow up to be a farmer, but Ike had other plans.

Ike liked business, the bigger the better, especially if it involved computers. So after graduating from the University of Minnesota, he worked with IBM, then Archer Daniels Midland, and then First Bank System. After forty-three years in the corporate world, Ike decided to work with Third World companies to teach them about information systems. He became a volunteer in the International Executive Service Corps.

Globe-trotter Ike has served in Singapore, El Salvador, Jamaica, Peru, Indonesia, Honduras, and Ukraine. His current mission is helping orphaned African children, particularly those whose parents have died of AIDS. To raise funds for this project, Ike volunteer teaches technologically challenged people how to use a computer in return for donations to World

Visions, the organization spearheading the project in Africa.

According to his daughter Chris, the most exciting thing Bill McGowan ever did was "try a new piece of pie at Baker's Square." Then he turned 80 and Bill decided it was high time he did all the things he ever wanted to do. So to celebrate his eighth decade, he bungie-jumped. At 82, he celebrated his birthday with a sky dive. The next year, he was up in a glider, then it was a hot air balloon ride, and then a helicopter ride over the Grand Canyon.

One more thing—Bill McGowan walks three miles a day and lifts weights at his local YMCA.

When I announced in my column that I was writing this book, I asked my readers for candidates for this team. To my surprise, it was women who wrote in, not men. They nominated their husbands, brothers, and fathers. Typical of the wives was Virginia Bingham of Gustine, CA, who said her 84-year-old husband is groundskeeper for their church and also tends his own vegetable garden, and "It's big enough to feed half the town." Virginia closed her letter by observing that her husband also loves to play golf, but he was too busy to find the time.

So it goes with these older men. They're too busy plowing new ground to notice their advanced age. Not only are they outrageous, they're also a hidden resource and a boon to this country.

Who are your candidates for an "All-Outrageous" team? Send your selections, along with your rationales for picking them, to me at the addresses listed at the beginning of this book. ◆

# *Staying*

## *THE COURSE*

*"For age is opportunity no less*
*Than youth itself, though in another dress*
*And as the evening twilight fades away*
*The sky is filled with stars invisible by day."*

—Henry Wadsworth Longfellow

We close then as we opened, reaffirming that to be consistently outrageous in our society is to be vital and involved and, importantly, to continue in the traditional male role as a contributor to life.

Speaking on behalf of the Society of Outrageous Older Men, I welcome you to our expanding membership and suggest there are certain things you may elect to do in order to keep your franchise active and rewarding.

It is an accepted fact that Americans are never comfortable for long without some new crusade (global warming, the disappearance of the tiger) to test their mettle. One way for you to campaign or crusade is to keep handy a list of people and things to protest against. As a columnist, I am called upon from time to time to share my personal causes. Bear in mind, it is the rare and oddball journalist who regularly monitors the human parade and doesn't accumulate a few pet issues.

These are my top ten hot buttons. You're welcome to join in my outrage.

1. I deplore books and magazine articles that guarantee you can live longer, better, richer, and retire to Happy Valley simply by reading 318 pages of "foolproof, practical tips to fight wrinkles, hair loss, prostate trouble, impotence, stress, insomnia, and more." That line is a direct quote from the jacket copy of a book called *Look 10 Years Younger, Live 10 Years Longer* published by Prentice-Hall. This type of hucksterism is an insult to your intelligence as well as mine.

2. Telemarketers and other swindlers who prey upon older Americans make me wish the penal system still had wooden stocks in public squares. I think a week in one of those wooden torture machines would eliminate some repeat offenders. As it is, the scam crowd just pays a fine and moves along to another location, always staying two steps ahead of the local sheriff. Remember, if it sounds too good to be true, it almost certainly is—especially if it involves money.

3. To all those members of Congress and other regulators who argue that we have too many rules and regulations governing nursing homes, I offer one suggestion: pretend you're a Medicaid patient and stay in a nursing home for one month. Then we'll listen to your suggestions.

4. I further confess an antipathy to young automobile drivers who salute me with an outstretched middle finger, a gesture commonly known as "flipping the bird." Isn't leaning

on your horn enough of an assault on my senses?

5. I hold in contempt the business leaders who downsize, throwing thousands of seniors out of work, and then brag about their record years to their stockholders. I also get a bad taste from warm and fuzzy stories about older men who are forced to work in some fast food joint at the minimum wage. If the job market were fairer, many of these retirees would be able to find work that was suitable and paid a decent wage.

6. I find tedious those older men who still smoke cigarettes, slavishly follow a high fat diet ("You only go around once!"), take no exercise, and then loudly complain about the miseries of their old age. What did they expect? That a free lunch came with a lifetime guarantee? Growing older is no circus. It tests us all.

7. People with no sense of humor should be required to watch old Sid Caesar television shows followed by tapes featuring Jonathan Winters, Carol Burnett, Charlie Chaplin, Jack Benny, Laurel and Hardy, Johnny Carson, and Robin Williams.

    Following this homework, they should be sent to work as teachers' aides in a pre-school nursery to foster intergenerational good will.

8. As a tenacious foe of ageism, I deplore the Federal Aviation Administration's ruling that pilots must retire at the age of 60. As of this writing, some 30,000 of the 113,500 commercial pilots are between the ages of 50 and 59. We simply cannot afford to lose these veteran aviators. Congress, are you listening?

    If we must, let's judge each pilot on his or her individual work and health records.

9. Older men who appoint themselves vigilantes and dash around condo complexes enforcing far too many rules and regulations are a nuisance. In the modest south Florida condo my family jointly owns, there is a certain pest who, despite beastly temperatures and the world class humidity, reminds people to always have something on their feet, to cover their entire anatomy (tank tops don't do the job for this sidewalk superintendent), not to carry beverage glasses to the pool area.

   At a time in life when these self-appointed sheriffs should be kicking back and relaxing, they go out of their way to be objectionable—and give seniors a bad name. This negative behavior, by the way, does not constitute a form of outrageousness. What is outrageous is that we allow these meddlers to persist in their petty, officious behavior.

10. I remain intolerant of intolerance of every stripe. As I have taken pains to emphasize, I am particularly cranky about ageism. I want older Americans everywhere to be proud, confident, vocal about their contributions. The next time you attend a concert or a play or visit a museum, look around you. Notice all the gray heads? In lamenting the declining attendance at arts events, Richard A. Peterson of Vanderbilt University pointed out it was the Depression and World War II babies who always have been the most enthusiastic supporters and patrons. "They go to concerts, ballet, opera, all theater. They just go," he states, "until they're deaf and their teeth fall out." That's us, good citizens until it hurts.

Whatever you think of my list of peeves and dislikes, I hope you'll soon get started on your own list. Consider this an assignment as you go forward under the banner of Outrageous Older Man. If you elect, send me your list and perhaps we can join forces on an issue. Write me at the addresses listed in the front of this book.

Now, I wish you long life and suggest that you take strength from this timeless wisdom handed down by poets, orators, philosophers, and historians of all nations: It is not achievement that counts, but rather the unremitting *effort* to achieve which marks the successful life.

"I have regrets but there are not many of them and, fortunately, I forget what they are," said author William Maxwell as he approached his 90th birthday. Excellent advice. Our pursuit of happiness never ends.

Like you, I have things to do, new journeys to plan. I mean to take a whitewater rafting trip. I also want to travel to Africa with my wife, the animal lover, to see wild animals while a few remain upright. I desperately need to take a computer course because I shall continue cranking out two syndicated columns a week, and plan on writing another book. It's still my ambition to compete as a swimmer in the Georgia Senior Olympics. I'd like to learn more about gardening and cooking. I genuinely wish to take dance lessons as a gift to a patient spouse, maybe after I've lost those ten pounds I keep on a permanent "to do" list. Moreover, I want to see my beloved grandchildren grow, be happy, and continue to make me laugh. I need to fill out my organ donor card, and I want to live long enough to see medical science wrestle Alzheimer's to the mat. Just delaying the onset for five, ten years would be a breakthrough to celebrate.

With all this on the agenda, this outrageous fellow had best get started. You're coming, too, aren't you?

*Ageless Body, Timeless Mind: The Quantam Alternative To Growing Old* by Deepak Chopra, M.D. (Harmony Books, 1993)

*Aging: An Exploration* by David P. Barash (University of Washington Press, 1983)

*Aging, Concepts and Controversies* by Harry R. Moody (Pine Forge Press, 1998)

*Anatomy of an Illness as Perceived by the Patient: Reflections on Healing and Regeneration* by Norman Cousins (W.W. Norton, 1979)

*Angela's Ashes: A Memoir* by Frank McCourt (Scribner, 1996)

*Be An Outrageous Older Woman* by Ruth Harriet Jacobs, Ph.D. (Knowledge, Ideas & Trends, Inc., 1st edition, 1993)

*Biomarkers: The 10 Determinants of Aging You Can Control* by William Evans, Ph.D., and Irwin H. Rosenberg, M.D., with Jacqueline Thompson (Simon & Schuster, 1991)

*Brain in Human Aging, The* by Gene Cohen, M.D., Ph.D. (Springer Publishing Company, 1988)

*Broken Heart: The Medical Consequences of Loneliness, The* by James J. Lynch, M.D. (Basic Books, 1977)

*Coming of Age: the Story of Our Century by Those Who've Live It* by Studs Terkel (New Press, 1995)

*Enjoy Old Age: A Program Of Self-Management* by B.F. Skinner and M.E. Vaughan (W. W. Norton & Company, 1983)

*Fifty To Forever* by Hugh Downs (Thomas Nelson Publishers, 1994)

*Full-time RVing: A Complete Guide to Life on the Open Road* by Bill and Jan Moeller (Trailer Life Books, 1993)

*Harvest Moon: Portrait of a Nursing Home* by Sallie Tisdale (Henry Holt and Company, 1987)

*Having Our Say: The Delany Sisters' First 100 Years* by Sarah and A. Elizabeth Delany with Amy Hill Hearth (Kodansha International, 1993)

*Head First: The Biology of Hope and the Healing Power of the Human Spirit* by Norman Cousins (Penguin Books, 1990)

*How A Man Ages* by Curtis Pesman and the Editors of *Esquire* (Esquire Press, 1984)

*How And Why We Age* by Leonard Hayflick, Ph.D. (Ballantine Books, 1994)

*How to Find Love, Sex and Intimacy after 50: A Woman's Guide* by Mattie Gershenfeld, M.D. and Judith Newman (Fawcett Columbine, 1991)

*How to Get Married Again: the Surefire Guide to Finding a New Mate* by Harriete Ryder (Ballantine Book, 1975)

*In My Father's Garden* by Lee May (Longstreet Press, Inc., 1995)

*Inside The Brain: Revolutionary Discoveries of How the Mind Works* by Ron Kotulak (Andrews and McMeel Publishing, 1996)

*Intoxicated By My Illness: And Other Writings on Life and Death* by Anatole Broyard (Fawcett Columbine, 1992)

*Joy of Sex, The: A Cordon Bleu Guide to Lovemaking* edited by Alex Comfort, M.B., Ph.D. (Crown, 1972)

*Late Love: A Celebration of Marriage After Fifty* by Eileen Simpson (Houghton Mifflin Company, 1994)

*Leaving Birmingham: Notes of a Native Son* by Paul Hemphill (Viking, 1993)

*Legacies* edited by Maury Leibovitz and Linda Solomon (Harper-Collins, 1993)

*Look 10 Years Younger, Live 10 Years Longer: A Man's Guide* (Prentice-Hall, 1995)

*Love and Sex after 60* by Robert Butler, M.D. and Myrna Lewis, M.S.W. (Ballantine Books, revised edition, 1993)

*Love in the Time of Cholera* by Gabriel Garcia Marquez (Viking/Penguin, 1989)

*Male Machine, The* by Marc Feigen Fasteau (McGraw-Hill, 1974)

*Methuselah Factors, The: Learning from the World's Longest Living People* by Dan Georgakas (Academy Chicago Publishers, revised and updated, 1995)

*Myth of Senility, The: The Truth About the Brain and Aging* by Robin Marantz Henig (An American Association of Retired Persons publication: Scott, Foresman and Co., updated and revised edition, 1988)

*Nursing Homes: Getting Good Care There* by Sarah Greene Burger, R.N., Virginia Fraser, Sara Hunt, and Barbara Frank (American Source Books, 1996)

*Over The Hills: A Midlife Escape Across America By Bicycle* by David Lamb (Time Books, 1996)

*Personal Best: The Foremost Philosopher of Fitness Shares Techniques for Success and Self-Liberation* by George Sheehan, M.D. (Rodale Press, 1989)

*Prostate: A Guide for Men and the Women Who Love Them, The* by Patrick Walsh, M.D. and Janet Farrar Worthington (The Johns Hopkins University Press, 1995)

*Prostate & Cancer: A Family Guide to Diagnosis, Treatment & Survival* by Sheldon Marks, M.D. (Fisher Books, 1995)

*Prostate Book: Sound Advice on Symptoms and Treatment, The* Stephen N. Rous, M.D., (W.W. Norton & Company, 1988)

*Say Yes To Old Age: Developing a Positive Attitude Toward Aging* by Alex Comfort (Crown Publishers, Inc., revised and updated, 1990)

*Secrets of Becoming a Late Bloomer: Extraordinary Ordinary People on the Art of Staying Creative, Alive and Aware in Mid-life and Beyond* by Connie Goldman and Richard Mahler (Stillpoint Publishing, 1995)

*Staying With It* by John Jerome (The Viking Press, 1984)

*Strangers On a Bridge* by James B. Donovan with Bard Lindeman (Atheneum, 1964)

*Survival of the RV Snowbirds* by Joe and Kay Peterson (available from Escapees Club, Livingston, TX, 77351, 1982)

*Taste of My Own Medicine, A: When the Doctor is the Patient* by Edward E. Rosenbaum, M.D. (Random House, 1988)

*Ten Million Steps* by Paul Reese and Joe Henderson (WRS Publishing, 1993)

*To Dance with the White Dog: A Novel* by Terry Kay (Peachtree Publishers, 1990)

*Twins Who Found Each Other, The* by Bard Lindeman (William Morrow and Company, 1969)

*Vital Involvement in Old Age* by Erik H. Erikson, Joan M. Erikson, and Helen Q. Kivnick (W.W. Norton & Company, 1986)

*We Live Too Short And Die Too Long* by Walter M. Bortz II, M.D. (Bantam Books, 1991)

*Widower, The* by Jane Burgess Kohn and Willard K. Kohn (Beacon Press, 1978)

*Why Survive?: Being Old In America* by Robert N. Butler, M.D. (Harper & Row Publishers, 1975)

*Will America Grow Up Before It Grows Old?: How the Coming Social Security Crisis Threatens You, Your Family and Your Country* by Peter G. Peterson (Random House, 1996)

*Wonderful Crisis of Middle Age, The: Some Personal Reflections* by Eda LeShan (David McKay Company, Inc., 1973)